VERDI

REQUIEM

for

Four Solo Voices and Chorus

Composed in memory of Alessandro Manzoni
and first performed at the Church of San Marco, Milan,
on 22nd May, 1874, under the direction of the composer.

VOCAL SCORE

With the original Latin text and
English translation by Geoffrey Dunn

RICORDI

Publishers' Note

The orchestral rehearsal numbers correspond to those in the revised miniature conductor's score; the orchestral *letters* to those in the original *folio conductor's score.*

The dynamics shown in brackets do not appear in Verdi's original score and are given as indications only.

Conductor's scores and orchestral parts are available on hire. Words only (LD403W) may be purchased.

Permission must be obtained from the publishers if it is wished to perform the work in this English translation. All enquiries to:

G. RICORDI & CO.
(London) Ltd.,
Kiln House
210 New Kings Road
London SW6 4NZ

Made and printed in England by
HALSTAN & CO. LTD. AMERSHAM, BUCKS

REQUIEM

No. 1. REQUIEM

Requiem aeternam dona eis Domine: et lux perpetua luceat eis.
Te decet hymnus, Deus, in Sion, et tibi redetur votum in Jerusalem: exaudi orationem meam, ad te omnis caro veniet.
Requiem aeternam dona eis, Domine: et lux perpetua luceat eis.

Kyrie eleison, Christe eleison.

Rest and peace eternal give them, Lord Our God ; and light for evermore shine down upon them.
Oh God, a hymn becomes Thee in Sion, and vows shall be rendered to Thee in Jerusalem : hear this my supplication, for all flesh shall come to Thee.
Rest and peace eternal grant them, Lord Our God ; and light for evermore shine down upon them.

Kyrie eleison, Christe eleison.

No. 2. DIES IRAE

Dies irae, dies illa,
Solvet saeclum in favilla,
Teste David cum Sybilla.
Quantus tremor est futurus,
Quando judex est venturus,
Cuncta stricte discussurus!

Day of anger, Day of terror,
All shall crumble into ashes,
This was David's revelation.
What a trembling shall possess them
When the Judge shall come to judgment,
Searching all the souls before Him !

TUBA MIRUM

Tuba mirum spargens sonum,
Per sepulchra regionum,
Coget omnes ante thronum.
Mors stupebit et natura,
Cum resurget creatura,
Judicanti responsura.

Trumpets sounding loud as thunder
Call the buried dead from slumber,
To the throne of God Almighty.
Death shall marvel, Earth shall wonder,
When departed generations
Rise again to answer judgment.

LIBER SCRIPTUS

Liber scriptus proferetur,
In quo totum continetur,
Unde mundus judicetur.
Judex ergo cum sedebit,
Quidquid latet apparebit,
Nil inultum remanebit.
Dies irae, dies illa,
Solvet saeclum in favilla,
Teste David cum Sybilla.

Open lies the book before them,
Where all records have been written,
When creation comes to trial.
Then the Lord shall sit in judgment,
What was hidden is uncovered,
Naught forgotten, naught unpunished.
Day of anger, Day of terror,
All shall crumble into ashes,
This was David's revelation.

QUID SUM MISER

Quid sum miser tunc dicturus,
Quem patronum rogaturus,
Cum vix justus sit securus!

What shall I plead in my anguish ?
Who will help me, give me counsel,
When the just are not acquitted ?

REX TREMENDAE

Rex tremendae majestatis,
Qui salvandos salvas gratis,
Salva me, fons pietatis.

King omnipotent and mighty,
King of dreadful power and glory,
Thou dost save the true repentant,
Save Thou me, Oh fount of mercy !

RECORDARE

Recordare, Jesu pie,
Quod sum causa tuae viae,
Ne me perdas illa die.
Quaerens me, sedisti lassus,
Redemisti crucem passus,
Tantus labor non sit cassus.
Juste judex ultionis,
Donum fac remissionis
Ante diem rationis.

Ah, remember, gentle Jesus,
'Twas for my sake Thou didst suffer.
On that day do not forsake me.
Seeking me Thou wast afflicted,
To redeem me by Thy Passion ;
Let such labour not be useless.
Just and upright Judge Almighty,
Grant me grace for my atonement
Ere the day I stand before Thee.

INGEMISCO

Ingemisco tanquam reus,
Culpa rubet vultus meus,
Supplicanti parce, Deus.
Qui Mariam absolvisti,
Et latronem exaudisti,
Mihi quoque spem dedisti.
Preces meae non sunt dignae,
Sed tu bonus fac benigne,
Ne perenni cremer igne.
Inter oves locum praesta,
Et ab hoedis me sequestra,
Statuens in parte dextra.

I lament, for I am guilty :
And I blush for my wrong-doing :
I implore Thee, Saviour, spare me.
Thou hast dried the tears of Mary,
And the robber won Thy pity,
So shall I, too, hope for pardon.
My petitions are unworthy,
Yet have mercy, do not send me
To the fire flaming for ever.
In Thy sheepfold let me enter,
Do not herd me with the guilty,
Set me there upon Thy right hand.

CONFUTATIS

Confutatis maledictis,
Flammis acribus addictis,
Voca me cum benedictis.
Oro supplex et acclinis,
Cor contritum quasi cinis,
Gere curam mei finis.
Dies irae, dies illa,
Solvet saeclum in favilla,
Teste David cum Sybilla.

When the cursèd all are banished,
Doomed to that devouring furnace,
Summon me among the blessèd.
On my knees I fall before Thee,
Sorrow turns my heart to ashes,
Grant me grace at my departing.
Day of anger, Day of terror,
All shall crumble into ashes,
This was David's revelation.

LACRYMOSA

Lacrymosa dies illa,
Qua resurget ex favilla,
Judicandus homo reus.
Huic ergo parce Deus.
Pie Jesu Domine,
Dona eis requiem !
Amen.

Day of bitter lamentation,
When man rises up from ashes,
Doomed to judgment, lost and guilty,
Then, Lord, pity this Thy servant.
Blessed Jesus, Christ Our Lord,
Saviour, grant them rest and peace.
Amen.

No.3. OFFERTORIO

Domine Jesu Christe, rex gloriae, libera animas omnium fidelium defunctorum de poenis inferni et de profundo lacu.

Libera eas de ore leonis, ne absorbeat eas tartarus, ne cadant in obscurum : sed signifer sanctus Michael repraesentet eas in lucem sanctam, quam olim Abrahae promisisti et semini ejus.

Lord of Lords, Jesus, Our Lord and Saviour Jesus Christ, King of Kings and King of Glory, free the souls of all the faithful departed from Hell and its torments, and from the soundless chasm.

Oh Lord, deliver them from the mouth ot the lion, that they may not be swallowed up by Hell and perish in its darkness: but may Michael raise his holy sign and lead them onward into Thy clear light of heaven, which Thou didst promise of old to Abraham and his seed to the last generation.

Hostias et preces tibi, Domine, laudis offerimus.	Sacrifice and prayers, Oh Lord, we offer Thee. Hear our prayers, Oh Lord, mingled with songs of praise.
Tu suscipe pro animabus illis, quarum hodie memoriam facimus, fac eas, Domine, de morte transire ad vitam, quam olim Abrahae promisisti et semini ejus.	Do Thou receive them for those souls departed, whom we this day here commemorate ; grant them, Oh Lord, to pass from death into life everlasting, which Thou didst promise of old to Abraham and his seed to the last generation.
Libera animas omnium fidelium defunctorum de poenis inferni et de profundo lacu, de morte transire ad vitam.	Oh Lord, deliver the souls of all the faithful departed from Hell and the dark pit, to pass out of death into life everlasting.

No.4. SANCTUS

Sanctus Dominus Deus Sabaoth,	Holy, holy, holy, Lord God of Sabaoth,
Pleni sunt coeli et terra gloria tua.	Earth and heaven are full of echoes to Thy glory.
Hosanna in excelsis !	Hosanna in the highest !
Benedictus, qui venit in nomine Domini.	Blessed is he that cometh in the name of the Lord of Lords.
Pleni sunt coeli et terra gloria tua.	Earth and heaven are full of echoes praising Thy glory.
Hosanna in excelsis !	Hosanna in the highest !

No.5. AGNUS DEI

Agnus Dei, qui tollis peccata mundi, dona eis requiem.	Lamb of God, Thou that bearest the world's wrong-doing, grant them, grant Thy servants rest for evermore.
Agnus Dei, qui tollis peccata mundi, dona eis requiem sempiternam.	Help Thy servants, grant that they may find rest and peace never-ending.

No.6. LUX AETERNA

Lux aeterna luceat eis, Domine, cum sanctis tuis in aeternum, quia pius es.	Light for ever shine down upon them, Christ the Lord, with all Thy blessed Saints in all ages, since Thou art just and good.
Requiem aeternam dona eis, Domine, et lux perpetua luceat eis.	Light that never fades shine down upon them with all Thy Saints for evermore, since Thou art just. Grant them rest and peace.

No.7. LIBERA ME

Libera me, Domine, de morte aeterna, in die illa tremenda; quando coeli movendi sunt et terra. Dum veneris judicare saeculum per ignem.	Lord, deliver me out of everlasting death, Oh Lord, upon that day of terror, when the earth and the heavens shall be shaken. When Thou shalt come and the whole world know the fire of judgment.
Tremens factus sum ego et timeo, dum discussio venerit atque ventura ira.	Trembling, frightened and full of despair am I, full of terror and great fear, till the trial shall be at hand, and the wrath to come.
Dies irae, dies illa, dies calamitatis et miseriae, dies magna et amara valde.	Day of anger, Day of terror, Day of disaster and of misery, Day most fearful, hopeless, and exceeding bitter.
Requiem aeternam dona eis, Domine, et lux perpetua luceat eis.	Rest and peace for ever, grant them rest and peace eternal, and light for evermore shine down upon them, Lord Our God.
Libera me, Domine, de morte aeterna, in die illa tremenda; quando coeli movendi sunt et terra. Dum veneris judicare saeculum per ignem.	Lord, deliver me out of everlasting death upon that day of terror, when the earth and the heavens shall be shaken, when Thou shalt come, then shall mankind know the fire of judgment.
Libera me, Domine, de morte aeterna, in die illa tremenda. Libera me, Domine.	Oh Lord, deliver me from death everlasting in that dread day of terror. Save me, Oh Lord.

Geoffrey Dunn

CONTENTS

No. 1. REQUIEM & KYRIE ELEISON

CHORUS STANDS until p. 50

(Rest and peace, and Lord have mercy)

Soprano, Mezzo-Soprano, Tenor, Bass and Chorus

Kiln House, 210 New Kings Road, London SW6 4NZ

Four Sopranos only
do - na, do - na e - is, Do - mi - ne:
give them, give them, give them, Lord Our God;
C.
T.
B.
CHORUS
con espressione
rinf.
S.
1
Tutti
sempre ppp
et lux per - pe-tu-a, et lux per - pe - tu - a
and light for ev-er-more, Thy light for ev - er-more
pp
C.
T.
B.
CHORUS
dolcissimo
ppp
rinf.

S.
C.
T.
B.
CHORUS
ppp
lu - ce - at e - is,
shine down up - on them,
lu - ce - at e - is.
shine down up - on them.
lu - ce - at
shine down up -
lu - ce - at e - is.
shine down up - on them
p
2
Poco più (♩ = 88)
lu - ce - at e - is.
shine down up - on them.
Te de - cet
Oh God, a
e - is.
- on them.
f
Te de - cet hym - nus, De - us, in
Oh God, a hymn be - comes Thee in
Te de - cet hym - nus, De - - us, in Si - on, et
Oh God, a hymn be - comes Thee in Si - on, and

S.
C.
T.
B.
CHORUS
f
dim.
ppp
cresc.
ff
Te de-cet hym - nus, De - - - - -
Oh God, a hymn be - comes
hym - nus, De - - - us, in Si - - - on, et
hymn be - comes Thee in Si - - - on, and
Si - on, et ti - bi red - de - tur vo - tum in Je -
Si - on, and to Thee shall vows be ren - dered in Je -
ti - bi, red - de - tur vo - tum in Je - ru - sa - lem:
vows un - to Thee be ren - dered in Je - ru - sa - lem.
us, in Si - on, et ti - bi red - de - tur vo - tum in Je - ru - sa -
Thee in Si - on, and vows shall be ren-dered to Thee in Je - ru - sa -
ti - bi red - de - tur ti - bi, red - de - tur vo - tum in Je - ru - sa -
vows shall be rendered to Thee, and vows be ren - dered in Je - ru - sa -
- ru - sa - lem: e - xau - di o - ra - ti - o - nem me - -
- ru - sa - lem. Oh, hear me, and hear my sup - pli - ca - -
e - xau - di o - ra - ti - o - nem me -
Oh, hear me, and hear my sup - pli - ca -

S.
p
f
- lem: e - xau - di o - ra - ti - o - nem me - am,
- lem. Oh Lord God, hear this my sup - pli - ca - tion,
C.
- lem: o - ra - ti - o - nem me - am,
- lem. Oh hear my sup - pli - ca - tion,
CHORUS
T.
- am, o - ra - ti - o - nem me - am, ad te
- tion; hear this my sup - pli - ca - tion, for all
B.
- am, o - ra - ti - o - nem me - am,
- tion; hear this my sup - pli - ca - tion,
S.
pp
dim. sempre
ad te om - nis ca - ro ve - ni - et.
for all flesh, all flesh shall come to Thee.
3
Attacca subito
(come prima)
C.
ad te om - nis ca - ro ve - ni - et.
for all flesh, all flesh shall come to Thee.
T.
om - nis ca - ro ve - ni - et.
flesh, all flesh shall come to Thee.
B.
ad te om - nis ca - ro ve - ni - et.
for all flesh, all flesh shall come to Thee.

S.
C.
B.
T.
CHORUS
pp sotto voce
il più piano possibile
Re - qui - em,
Rest and peace,
Re - qui - em æ - ter - nam,
Rest and peace e - ter - nal
pp

S.
C.
T.
B.
CHORUS
Four Sopranos only
do - na, do - na e - is, Do - mi - ne:
give them, give them, give them, Lord our God;
con espress.
rinf.

S.
C.
T.
B.
CHORUS
Tutti sempre ppp
sempre ppp
pp
et lux per - pe-tu - a, et lux per - pe - tu - a
and light for ev-er-more, Thy light for ev - er-more
ppp dolciss.
rinf.
p
lu - ce - at e - is, lu - ce - at e -
shine down up - on them, shine down up - on
lu - ce - at e -
shine down up - on
lu - ce - at e - - - -
shine down up - on
sempre cresc.

4
TENOR
Animando un poco
f
Ky - ri - e e - le - - - - - - i -
S.
- is.
them.
C.
- is.
them.
CHORUS
T.
- is.
them.
B.
- is.
them.
4
Animando un poco
p
cresc. a poco a poco
f
TEN.
- son,
BASS
f
Chri - ste, Chri - - ste e - le - - i -

SOPRANO
ben legato, largo, pesante
Ky - ri - e e - le - i - son, e - le - i -
BASS
- son,
pp
SOP.
- son, Ky - ri - e
MEZZO-SOP.
Chri - ste, Chri - ste e - le - i - - - -
TEN.
Ky - ri - - e
BASS
Ky - ri - e e - le - i -
pp

A
5
SOP.
cresc.
ff
e - le - i - - - - - - son,
MEZZO-SOP.
ff
- son, e - le - i - son, Ky - ri - e
TEN.
ff
Ky - - ri - e e - le - i - son,
BASS
ff
- son, e - le - i - son, Ky - ri - e
CHORUS
S.
ff
e - le - i - son,
C.
p
ff
e - - le - - i - son,
T.
pp
ff
Ky - - ri - e e - le - i - son,
B.
pp
ff
Ky - ri - e e - le - i - son,
A
5
ff
pp leggierissimo

SOP.
e - le - i - son,
MEZZO-SOP.
e - le - i - son,
TEN.
e - le - i -
BASS
S.
C.
pp
Ky - ri - e e -
CHORUS
T.
pp
Ky - ri - e e - le - i-son,
B.
pp
Ky - ri - e e - le - i-son,

SOP.
cantando
e - - - - le - i - son,
MEZZO-SOP.
Chri-ste e - le - i - -
TEN.
- son,
e - - - - -
BASS
e - le - i - son,
Chri - ste e - le - i -
S.
pp
Ky - ri - e e - le - i - son,
Chri - ste e -
C.
- le - i - son,
CHORUS
T.
pp
Chri
B.
pp
Chri
pp

SOP.
Chri - - - ste e-le - i - son Chri - - -
MEZZO-SOP.
-son, Chri-ste e - le - i - son Chri - -
TEN.
-le - i - son, Chri - - - ste e-le - i-son
BASS
-son Chri-ste e - le - i - son, Chri - ste,Chri - -
S.
-le - i - son, e-le-i-son,
C.
e-le-i-son,
T.
- - - - - - - - - ste
B.
- - - - - - - - - ste
CHORUS

B
6
SOP.
- ste e - le - i - son, e - le - i - son, e - le - i - son,
MEZZO-SOP.
- ste e - le - i - son, e - le - i - son, e - le - i - son, Ky - ri -
TEN.
e - - le - i - son,
BASS
- ste e - le - i - son, e - le - i - son, e - le - i - son,
S.
f
e - le - i - son,
C.
f
e - le - i - son,
CHORUS
T.
f
e - le - i - son,
B.
f
e - le - i - son,
B
6
ff
p

SOP.
MEZZO-SOP.
-e e - le - i - son, Ky - ri - e e - le - i - son,
TEN.
Ky - ri - e e - le - i - son, Ky - ri -
BASS
Ky - ri - e e - le - i - son,
S.
C.
CHORUS
T.
B.
f p f p

SOP.
ff
e - le - i - son, e - le - i -
MEZZO-SOP.
f
e - le - i - son, e - le - i - son, e - le - i -
TEN.
f
-e e - le - i-son, e-le-i-son, e-le-i-
BASS
f
Ky - - ri - e e - le - i - son, e - le - i -
CHORUS
S.
f
e - le - i - son, e - le - i -
C.
f
e - le - i - son, e - le - i -
T.
f
e-le-i-son, e-le-i-
B.
f
e - le - i - son, e - le - i -
ff

SOP.
ff
ppp
- son, e - le - i - son, e - le - i - son,
MEZZO-SOP.
ff
ppp
- son, e - le - i - son, e - le - i - son,
TEN.
3
ff
ppp
- son, e - le - i - son, e - le - i - son,
BASS
ff
ppp
- son, e - le - i - son, e - le - i - son,
CHORUS
S.
ff
Four Sopranos divisi
ppp
- son, e - le - i - son, e - le - i - son,
C.
ff
ppp Two Contraltos
- son, e - le - i - son, e - le - i - son,
T.
3
ff
Four Tenors divisi
ppp
- son, e - le - i - son, e - le - i - son,
B.
ff
Two Basses
ppp
- son, e - le - i - son, e - le - i - son,
ff
pp
pp
3

SOP.
MEZZO-SOP.
TEN.
BASS
S.
C.
T.
B.
CHORUS
7
p
espr.
p dolce
e - le - i - son,
Chri-ste e-le-i - son,
e - le - i -
e - le - i - son,
e - le - i - son,
e - le - i - son,
Ky - ri - e e - le - i-son,
Ky - ri - e e -
Chri - - - ste

SOP.
Chri - - - ste Chri - ste e - le - i -
MEZZO-SOP.
- son, Chri - - - ste e - le - i - son,
TEN.
Chri - - - ste e - le - i -
BASS
e - le - i - son, e -
CHORUS
S.
Ky - ri - e e - le - i-son, e - le - i -
C.
e - le - i - son,
T.
- le - - - i - son, e - le - i -
B.
e - - - le - i - son, e -
(cresc.)

SOP.
dim. ed allarg.
morendo
a tempo
pp
- son, Chri - ste,
MEZZO-SOP.
Chri - ste e - le - i - son, e - le - i - son, Chri - ste,
TEN.
- son,Chri - ste e - le - i - son, e - le - i - son, Chri - ste,
BASS
- le - - i - son, Chri - ste,
CHORUS
S.
ff
- son, e - le - i - son, Chri - ste,
C.
Chri - ste, e - le - i - son, e - le - i - son, Chri - ste,
T.
- son, Chri - ste e - le - i - son, e - le - i - son, Chri - ste,
B.
- le - - i - son, Chri - ste,
ff
dim. ed allarg.
a tempo
pp

SOP.
poco rall.
ppp
morendo
Chri - ste e - le - i - son.
MEZZO-SOP.
ppp
morendo
Chri - ste e - le - i - son.
TEN.
ppp
morendo
Chri - ste e - le - i - son.
BASS
ppp
morendo
Chri - ste e - le - i - son.
S.
poco rall.
ppp
morendo
Chri - ste e - le - i - son.
C.
ppp
morendo
Chri - ste e - le - i - son.
CHORUS
T.
ppp
morendo
Chri - ste e - le - i - son.
B.
ppp
morendo
Chri - ste e - le - i - son.
poco rall.
ppp
pp stacc. e leggiero
pp

No. 2. DIES IRAE

(Day of Anger)

S.
C.
T.
B.
CHORUS
ger,
ræ,
ff
Di - es il - la, di - es
Day of ter - ror, day of
8

8
S.
ter - - - - - - - - - ror,
il - - - - - - - - - la,
ff
Di - es il - - - - - - - la,
Day of ter - - - - - - - ror,
C.
ter - - - - - - - - - ror,
il - - - - - - - - - la,
ff
Di - es il - - - - - - - la,
Day of ter - - - - - - - ror,
T.
ter - - - - - - - - - ror,
il - - - - - - - - - la,
il - la, di - es il - - - - - la,
ter - ror, day of ter - - - - - ror,
B.
il - - - - - - - - - la,
ter - - - - - - - - - ror,
CHORUS
8
S.
f
Sol - vet sæ - clum in fa -
All shall crum - ble in - to
C.
f
Sol - vet sæ - clum in fa -
All shall crum - ble in - to
T.
f
Sol - vet, Sol - vet sæ - clum in fa -
All shall crum - ble, crum - ble in - to
B.
f
Sol - vet, Sol - vet sæ - clum in fa -
All shall crum - ble, crum - ble in - to
CHORUS
f

S.
C.
T.
B.
CHORUS
- vil - - - - la, Te - ste Da - vid cum Si -
ash - - - - es, this was Da - vid's rev - el -
- vil - - - - la, Te - ste, Te - ste Da-vid cum Si -
ash - - - - es, this was told in Da-vid's rev - el -
- vil - - - - la, Te - ste, Te - ste Da-vid cum Si -
ash - - - - es, this was told in Da-vid's rev - el -
9
ff
f
- byl - - - - la, Di - es,
- a - - - - tion, Day of
- byl - - - - la, Di - es Di - es
- a - - - - tion, Day, day, Day of
- byl - - - - la, Di - es i - ræ, Di - es
- a - - - - tion, Day of an - ger, Day of

CHORUS
S.
i - ræ, Di - es il - la,
an - ger, Day of ter - ror,
C.
i - ræ, Di - es il - la,
an - ger, Day of ter - ror,
T.
i - ræ, Di - es il - la,
an - ger, Day of ter - ror,
B.
i - ræ, Di - es il - la,
an - ger, Day of ter - ror,
CHORUS
S.
Sol - vet sæ - clum, Sol - vet in fa -
all shall crum - ble, mould - er in - to
C.
Sol - vet sæ - clum, Sol - vet in fa -
all shall crum - ble, mould - er in - to
T.
Sol - vet sæ - clum, Sol - vet in fa -
all shall crum - ble, mould - er in - to
B.
Sol - vet sæ - clum, Sol - vet in fa -
all shall crum - ble, mould - er in - to

S.
C.
T.
B.
CHORUS
- vil - la, Di - es, Di - es i - ræ,
ash - es, ash - es, ash - es, ash - es.
marc.
- vil - la, Di - es i - ræ, Di - es il - la, Sol - vet sæ - clum in fa -
ash - es, Day of an - ger, Day of ter - ror, all shall crum - ble in - to
pesante
- vil - la, Te - ste Da - vid cum Si - byl - la.
ash - es, this was Da - vid's rev - el - a - tion.
stent. un poco
a tempo

A
10
ff
S.
Di - es i - ræ, Di - es il - la,
Day of an - ger, Day of ter - ror,
C.
Di - es i - ræ, Di - es il - la,
Day of an - ger, Day of ter - ror,
T.
Di - es i - ræ, Di - es il - la,
Day of an - ger, Day of ter - ror,
B.
Di - es i - ræ, Di - es il - la,
Day of an - ger, Day of ter - ror,
CHORUS
S.
Sol - vet sæ - clum in fa - vil - la,
all shall crum - ble in - to ash - es,
C.
Sol - vet sæ - clum in fa - vil - la,
all shall crum - ble in - to ash - es,
T.
Sol - vet sæ - clum in fa - vil - la,
all shall crum - ble in - to ash - es,
B.
Sol - vet sæ - clum in fa - vil - la,
all shall crum - ble in - to ash - es,

CHORUS
S.
p
dim.
Di - es i - ræ, Di - es
Day of an - ger, Day of
C.
p dim.
Sol vet sæ - clum in fa - vil - la,
all shall crum - ble in - to ash - es,
T.
p dim.
Sol - vet sæ - clum in fa - vil - la,
all shall crum - ble in - to ash - es,
B.
p dim.
Sol - vet sæ - clum in fa - vil - la,
all shall crum - ble in - to ash - es,
p
dim.
CHORUS
S.
11
pp
il - la, Di - es i - ræ, Di - es
ter - ror, Day of an - ger, Day of
C.
p
pp
Te ste Da - vid cum Si - byl - la.
this was Da - vid's rev - el - a - tion.
T.
p
pp
Te - ste Da - vid cum Si - byl - la.
this was Da - vid's rev - el - a - tion.
B.
p
pp
Te - ste Da - vid cum Si - byl - la.
this was Da - vid's rev - el - a - tion.
11
ancora piu p
ancora dim.

SOP.
CHOR.
il - la.
ter - ror.
TEN. Soli
ppp cupo
Di - - es
Day of
pp sempre più piano
i - ræ.
an - ger.
CONT. Soli
pp cupo
Di - es i - ræ.
Day of an - ger.
SOP.
Soli
pp cupo
Di - es i - ræ.
Day of an - ger.
B
12
pp

S.
C.
T.
B.
CHORUS
pp sotto voce
Quan - tus tre - mor
What a trem-bling
est fu - tu - rus, Quan - do Ju - dex est ven-
shall pos - sess them, when the Judge shall come to

S.
C.
T.
B.
CHORUS
- tu - rus, Cun - cta stri - cte dis - cus - su - -
judg - ment, search - ing all the souls be - fore
ppp
C
13
Allegro sostenuto (♩ = 88)
- rus!
him!
Trumpets in the Orchestra
mf
pp
Trumpets afar
in the Orch.

pp
afar
p in the Orch.
pp
afar
afar
m.s. 3 2 1
m.s.
m.s.
m.s.
in the Orch.
poco cresc.
animando a poco a poco
m.d.
cresc. a poco a poco
D
14
tutta forza
ff
sempre animando

S.
sempre animando a poco a poco
ff
Tu - - -
Trum - - -
C.
CHORUS
T.
B.
ff
Tu - - - ba mi - rum spar - gens so - num,
Trum - - - pets sound - ing loud as thun - der,
12
12
12
6
afar
3
ff sempre animando a poco a poco
S.
- ba mi - - - rum
- pets sound - - - ing
C.
CHORUS
T.
B.
Tu - ba mi - rum spar - gens
Trum - pets sound - ing loud as

animando sempre sino alla
S.
spar - - - gens so - - -
loud as thun - - -
C.
ff
spar - gens so - - -
loud as thun - - -
T.
ff
spar - gens so - - -
loud as thun - - -
B.
so - num, Per se - pul - chra re - gi - o - - -
thun - der call the bur - ied dead from slum - - -
ff animando sempre sino alla
CHORUS
fine, ma sempre poco a poco
E
15
- - - num,
- - - der,
- - - num,
- - - der,
- - - num,
- - - der,
- - - num,
- - - ber,
Tu - ba
Trum - pets
Trumpets afar
Orchestra
fine, ma sempre poco a poco

CHORUS
S.
spar - gens___ so - num,
loud___ as___ thun - der,
C.
spar - gens___ so - num,
loud___ as___ thun - der,
T.
spar - gens
loud as
B.
mi - rum.___
sound - ing___
afar
S.
re - gi - o - num,
dead___ from___ slum - ber,
C.
re - gi - o - num,
dead___ from___ slum - ber,
T.
so - num,
thun-der,
Co - get
to the
B.
Per se - pul - chra___
call the bur - ied___
afar

S.
C.
T.
B.
CHORUS
ff
om
might
Down from tenor
thro
om - nes an - te
throne of God Al - might
secca
- nes.
- y.
- num.
16
Molto meno mosso (♩ = 72)
SIT
Bass Solo
Mors stu-
Death shall
ppp
tronca
con 8va sotto

BASS
-pe-bit, Mors stu-pe-bit et na-tu-ra, Cum re-
mar-vel, Death shall mar-vel, Earth shall won-der when de-
ppp
con 8va sotto
BASS
-sur-get cre-a-tu-ra, Ju-di-can-ti re-spon-
-part-ed gen-er-a-tions rise a-gain to an-swer
ppp
con 8va sotto
BASS
-su-ra.
judg-ment.
pp
Mors,
Death,
con 8va sotto
BASS
Mors, Mors stu-pe-bit.
Death, Death shall mar-vel.
ppp
con 8va sotto

F
17
Allegro molto sostenuto (♩ = 88)
MEZZO-SOP.
dim.
pp
Li - ber scri - ptus pro - fe - re - tur,
O - pen lies the book be - fore them
p
pp
ppp
In quo to - tum con - ti - ne - tur,
Where all rec - ords have been writ - ten,
f
Un - - de mun - dus, Un - de
When cre - - - a - tion, When cre -
mf
mun - dus ju - di - ce - tur, Un - de
a - tion comes to tri - al, When cre -
mun - dus, Un - de mun - dus ju - di - ce - - - - -
a - tion, When cre - a - tion comes to tri - - - - -
col canto

MEZZO-SOP.
18
in tempo
ff
- tur.
- al.
Ju - -
Then
SOP.
pppp con voce cupa e tristissima
Di - es i - ræ!
Day of an - ger!
CONT.
pppp
estremamente piano
TEN.
BASS
CHORUS
p
f
ff
pp
dex er - go cum se - de - bit,
the Lord shall sit in judg - ment,
cresc.
Quid - - - quid la - tet ap - pa - re - -
What was hid - den is un - co -

MEZZO-SOP.
19
- bit, Nil i - nul - tum re - ma -
- vered, Naught for - got - ten, naught un -
S.
sempre ppp
Di - es i - ræ!
Day of an - ger!
C.
sempre ppp
Di - es i - ræ!
Day of an - ger!
sotto voce
T.
sempre ppp
Di - es i - ræ!
Day of an - ger!
B.
sempre ppp
Di - es i - ræ!
Day of an - ger!
CHORUS
19
dolce
p
MEZZO-SOP.
poco accelerando
- ne - bit, Quid - quid la - tet ap - pa - re - bit, Nil i - nul - tum, Nil i -
- pun - ished, What was hid - den is un - co - vered, Naught for - got - ten, naught un -
p
poco accelerando
p
MEZZO-SOP.
mf a tempo
- nul - - tum re - - ma - - -
- pun - - ished, naught un - - -
mf a tempo

MEZZO-SOP.
-ne - bit, re - ma - ne - bit, Nil i-
-pun - ished, naught un - pun - ished, Naught for-
f
f
MEZZO-SOP.
un poco
20
-nul - tum Nil i - nul - tum re - ma - ne - - bit. Li - ber
- got - ten, naught for-got - ten, naught un - pun - - ished. O - pen
p
p
MEZZO-SOP.
scri - ptus pro - fe - re - tur, In quo
lies the book be - fore them where the
cresc.
MEZZO-SOP.
to - tum con - ti - ne - tur, Un - - - de
world's account is writ - ten, when cre-
cresc. sempre

MEZZO-SOP.
ff
mun - dus ju - di - ce - - - - - - - -
- a - tion comes to tri - - - - - - - -
8
ff
6
MEZZO-SOP.
pp
- tur. Ju - dex er - go cum se - de - bit, Quid - quid
- al. Then the Lord shall sit in judg - ment, What was
S.
pp con voce cupa e tristissima
Di - es i - ræ!
Day of an - ger!
C.
estremamente piano
pp
Di - es i - ræ!
Day of an - ger!
T.
pp
Di - es i - ræ!
Day of an - ger!
B.
pp
Di - es i - ræ!
Day of an - ger!
CHORUS
ppp
MEZZO-SOP.
21
ppp
la - tet ap - pa - re - bit, Nil i - nul - tum
hid - den is un - co - vered, Naught for - got - ten
21
ancora più p

MEZZO-SOP.
sempre più p
morendo
re-ma-ne-bit,
or un-pun-ished,
Nil,
Naught,
Nil,
naught,
Nil!
naught!
perdendosi
vuota
MEZZO-SOP.
ff
a tempo
Li - ber scri-ptus pro - fe - re - - tur.
O - pen lies the book be - fore them.
S.
C.
T.
B.
CHORUS
sempre cupo e pianissimo
Di - es i - ræ!
Day of an - ger!
STAND
ff
p col canto
a tempo
6

S.
Di - es i - ræ!
Day of an - ger!
C.
Di - es i - ræ!
Day of an - ger!
CHORUS
T.
Di - es i - ræ!
Day of an - ger!
B.
Di - es i - ræ!
Day of an - ger!
pp
S.
Di - es i - ræ!
Day of an - ger!
C.
Di - es i - ræ!
Day of an - ger!
CHORUS
T.
Di - es i - ræ!
Day of an - ger!
B.
Di - es i - ræ!
Day of an - ger!

6
G
22 Allegro agitato (come prima)
Lo Stesso movimento
tra le sei e le otto note
cresc.
f
S.
C.
T.
B.
CHORUS
ff
Di - es i - ræ, Di - es il - la,
Day of an - ger, Day of ter - ror,
Di es i - ræ, Di - es il - la,
Day of an - ger, Day of ter - ror,

S.
C.
T.
B.
CHORUS
Sol - vet sæ - clum in fa - vil - la,
all shall crum - ble in - to ash - es,
23
p dim.
Di - es i - ræ, Di - es
Day of an - ger, Day of
p
dim.

S.
il - la, Di - es i - ræ, Di - es
ter - ror, Day of an - ger, Day of
C.
Te - ste Da - vid cum Si - byl - la.
this was Da - vid's rev - el - a - tion,
T.
Te - ste Da - vid cum Si - byl - la.
this was Da - vid's rev - el - a - tion,
B.
Te - ste Da - vid cum Si - byl - la.
this was Da - vid's rev - el - a - tion,
CHORUS
ancora dim.
S.
pp
i - ræ, Di - es il - la, Di - es
an - ger, Day of ter - ror, Day of
C.
pp
Di - es il - la, Di - es
Day of ter - ror, Day of
T.
pp
Di - es il - la, Di - es
Day of ter - ror, Day of
B.
pp
Di - es il - la, Di - es
Day of ter - ror, Day of
CHORUS

S.
C.
T.
B.
CHORUS
i - - - ræ, Di - es i - -
an - - - ger, Day of an - -
dim.
- - - - - - - - - - - ræ.
- - - - - - - - - - - ger.
p
morendo

24
CHORUS SITS
MEZZO-SOP.
Adagio (♪. = 100)
espress.
Quid sum
What shall
pp
mi - - - - - ser tunc dic - tu - rus,
I plead in my an - guish?
Quem pa - tro - - - - -
Who will help
- num ro - ga - tu - rus, Cum vix ju - - - - -
me, give me coun - sel, when the just
col canto
p

MEZZO-SOP.
ben legato e dolce
-stus sit se - cu - - - - rus?
are not ac - quit - - - - ted?
TENOR
Quid sum mi - - - ser tunc dic -
What shall I plead in my
SOPRANO
Quem pa - tro - num ro - ga - tu - -
Who will help me, who will guide
MEZZO-SOP.
Quid sum, Quid sum mi - -
What then, what shall I
TENOR
pp
- tu - rus? Quid sum, Quid sum mi - -
an - guish? What then, what shall I

SOPRANO
dolce e legato
- rus, Cum vix ju - - - - - stus sit se -
me, when the just are not ac -
MEZZO-SOP.
- ser tunc dic - tu - rus?
plead in my an - guish?
TENOR
- ser tunc dic - tu - - - - - rus?
plead in my an - - - - - guish?
H
25
SOP.
pp
- cu - - - - - rus? Quem pa -
-quit - - - - - ted? Who will
MEZZO-SOP.
pp
Quid sum mi - ser, Quem pa - tro - num ro - ga -
In my an - guish, On whom shall I call for
TEN.
pp
Quid sum mi - ser, Quem pa -
In my an - guish, who can -
25 H
pp

SOP.
- tro - num, Quem pa - tro - num ro - ga -
help, who, who will help me, give me
MEZZO-SOP.
- tu - rus, Quem pa - tro - num ro - ga - tu - -
coun - sel, who can help me in my great
TEN.
- tro - num, Quem pa - tro - num ro - ga - tu - -
help me, who can help me in my great
SOP.
- tu - rus, Cum vix ju - - - - - stus sit se -
coun - sel, when the just are not ac -
MEZZO-SOP.
rus, Cum vix ju - - - - - stus sit se -
need? When the just are not ac -
TEN.
- rus, Cum vix ju - - - - - stus sit se -
need? When the just are not ac -
pp

SOP.
26
pp
- cu - - - - rus? Quid sum - mi -
- quit - - - - ted? What shall I
MEZZO-SOP.
pp
- cu - - - - rus? Quid sum - mi -
-quit - - - - ted? What shall I
TEN.
pp
- cu - - - - rus? Quid sum - mi -
- quit - - - - ted? What shall I
26
pp
SOP.
- ser - - - - - tunc dic - tu - rus? Quid
plead in my an - guish? What,
MEZZO-SOP.
- ser - - - - - tunc dic - tu - rus? Quid
plead in my an - guish? What,
TEN.
- ser, Quid sum mi - ser tunc dic-tu - rus? Quid
plead, in such grief and bit - ter an - guish? What,

dolce
SOP.
sum mi - ser
what shall I
MEZZO-SOP.
sum mi - ser, Quid sum mi - ser
what have I, what have I to
TEN.
sum mi - ser, Quid sum mi - ser
what have I, what have I to
TURN
CHORUS RISES
SOP.
tunc dic - tu - rus? Quid sum,
plead in an - guish? What? What?
MEZZO-SOP.
tunc dic - tu - rus? Quid sum, mi - ser,
plead in an - guish? In my an - guish,
TEN.
tunc dic - tu - rus? Quid sum, Quid sum
plead in an - guish? What? What? What have
f

SOP.
Cum vix
when the
MEZZO-SOP.
Quem pa - tro - num ro - ga - tu - rus,
when the just are not ac - quit - ted?
TEN.
mi - ser tunc dic - tu rus?
I to plead in an - guish?
SOP.
ju - stus sit se - cu - rus?
just are not ac - quit - ted?
27
Adagio maestoso (♩ = 72)
CHORUS
BASS
ff
Rex tre - men - dæ ma - je - sta - -
King om - ni - po - tent and migh - -
TENORS
pp
Rex tre - men - dæ ma - je - sta - tis!
King of dread - ful pow'r and glo - ry!
BASSES
pp
- tis!
- ty!
Rex tre - men - dæ ma - je -
King om - ni - po - tent and
ppp

BASS
dolce
Sal - va me, fons pi - e -
Save Thou me, Oh fount of
T.
CHORUS
pp
Qui sal - van - dos sal - vas gra - tis,
Thou dost save the true re - pen - tant,
B.
pp
- sta - tis!
migh - ty!
ppp
SOP.
28
Sal - va me,
Save Thou me,
Sal - va me,
Save Thou me,
MEZZO-SOP.
Sal - va me, fons pi - e - ta - tis!
Save Thou me, Oh fount of mer - cy!
TEN.
Sal - va me, fons pi - e -
save Thou me, Oh fount of
BASS
- ta - tis!
mer - cy!
28

SOP.
mf
Sal - va me, Sal - - va -
Save Thou me, Save Thou
MEZZO-SOP.
p
Sal - va
Save Thou
TEN.
- ta - tis!
mer - cy,
p
Sal - va
Save Thou
BASS
p
Sal - va
Save Thou
CHORUS
S.
ff
Sal - va me,
Save Thou me,
C.
ff
Sal - va me,
Save Thou me,
T.
ff
Sal - va me,
Save Thou me,
B.
ff
Rex tre-men-dæ ma - je - sta - tis!
King om-ni - po-tent and migh - ty!
ff
(mp)
8

SOP.
me, Sal - - va me,
me, Save Thou me,
MEZZO-SOP.
me, Sal - va me,
me, Save Thou me,
TEN.
me, Sal - va me,
me, Save Thou me,
BASS
me, Sal - va me,
me, Save Thou me,
CHORUS
S.
ff
Sal - va me, Sal - va
Save Thou me, Save Thou
C.
ff
Sal - va me, Sal - va
Save Thou me, Save Thou
T.
ff
Sal - va me, Sal - va
Save Thou me, Save Thou
B.
ff
Rex tre-men-dæ ma - je - sta - tis! Qui sal-van-dos sal - vas
King of dread-ful pow'r and glo - ry! Thou dost save the true re-
(ff)
(mp)
(ff)

SOP.
ff
fons pi - e - ta - tis! Sal - va,
Fount of com - pas - sion! Save me,
MEZZO-SOP.
Sal - va me, Sal - va,
Save Thou me, Save me,
TEN.
Sal - va me, Sal - va,
Save Thou me, Save me,
BASS
Sal - va me, Sal - va,
Save Thou me, Save me,
CHORUS
S.
me, Sal - va, Sal - va,
me, Save me, Save me,
C.
me, Sal - va, Sal - va,
me, Save me, Save me,
T.
me, Sal - va, Sal - va,
me, Save me, Save me,
B.
gra - tis, Sal - va, Sal - va me, Sal - va, Sal - va me,
pen - tant, Save - me, Save me, Lord, Save me, Save me, Lord,
(mp)

J
29
SOP.
Sal - va, Sal - - - va me,
Save me, Save Thou me,
MEZZO-SOP.
pp
Sal - - va
Save me, Save Thou
TEN.
Sal - va,
Save me,
BASS
Sal - va,
Save me,
CHORUS
S.
Sal - va,
Save me,
C.
Sal - va,
Save me,
T.
Sal - va,
Save me,
B.
Sal - va me, fons pi - e - ta - tis!
Save Thou me, Oh fount of mer - cy!
ppp

SOP.
Sal - - - va, Sal - va
Save me, Save Thou
MEZZO-SOP.
- ta - tis! Sal - va,
- pas - sion! Save Thou
TEN.
Sal - va me fons pi - e - ta - tis! Sal - - va
Save Thou me, Oh fount of mer - cy! Save Thou
BASS
Sal - va me, fons pi - e - ta - tis! Sal -
Save Thou me, Oh fount of mer - cy! Save
CHORUS
S.
Sal - va me,
Save Thou me,
C.
Sal - va me,
Save Thou me,
T.
Sal - va me,
Save Thou me,
B.
Sal - va me,
Save Thou me,
m.s.

SOP.
animando poco a poco
ff
me, fons pi - e - ta - tis! Sal - - va
me, Oh fount of mer - cy! Save Thou
MEZZO-SOP.
ff
me, fons pi - e - ta - tis! Sal - - va
me, Oh fount of mer - cy! Save Thou
TEN.
ff
me, fons pi - e - ta - tis! Sal - - va
me, Oh fount of mer - cy! Save Thou
BASS
ff
- va, Sal - va me, Rex tre - men - dæ ma - je - -
me, Save Thou me, King of dread-ful pow'r and
CHORUS
S.
ff
animando poco a poco
Sal - - va me,
Save Thou me,
C.
ff
Sal - - va me,
Save Thou me,
T.
ff
Sal - - va me,
Save Thou me,
B.
ff
Rex tre - men - dæ ma - je - sta - tis!
King om - ni - po - tent and migh - ty!
animando poco a poco
ff

30
sempre animando
SOP.
me, Sal - - - va me,
me, Save Thou me,
MEZZO-SOP.
me, Sal - - - va me,
me, Save Thou me,
TEN.
me, Sal - - - va me,
me, Save Thou me,
BASS
- sta - tis! Rex tre-men-dæ ma - je - - sta - tis!
glo - ry! King of dread-ful pow'r and glo - ry!
CHORUS
S.
Sal - - va me, Sal - - va
Save Thou me, Save Thou
C.
Sal - - va me, Sal - - va
Save Thou me, Save Thou
T.
Sal - - va me, Sal - - va
Save Thou me, Save Thou
B.
Rex tre-men-dæ ma - je - sta - tis! Qui sal-van-dos sal - vas
King om-ni - po-tent and migh - ty! Thou dost save the true re-
30
sempre animando

SOP.
Sal - - - va, Sal - - - -
Save me, Save
MEZZO-SOP.
Sal - - - va, Sal - va,
Save me, Save Thou
TEN.
Sal - - - va, Sal - va,
Save me, Save Thou
BASS
Qui sal-van-dos sal-vas gra - tis, Sal - va, Sal - va
Thou dost save the true re - - pent - ant, Save me, Save Thou
CHORUS
S.
me, Sal - - va me,
me, Save Thou me,
C.
me, Sal - - va me,
me, Save Thou me,
T.
me, Sal - - va me,
me, Save Thou me,
B.
gra - tis, Sal - va me, fons pi - e - ta - tis!
pent - ant, Save Thou me, Oh fount of mer - cy!

sempre animando
SOP.
- va, Sal - - - - - - - va,
me, Ah me,
MEZZO-SOP.
me, Sal - - va me, fons pi - - e-
me, Save Thou me, Oh fount of
TEN.
me, fons pi - e - ta - tis! Sal - va,
me, Oh fount of mer - cy! Save me,
BASS
me, fons pi - e - ta - tis! Sal - va me, Sal - - va,
me, Oh fount of mer - cy! Save Thou me, Save Thou
CHORUS
S.
ff
Sal - - - - - - - va me, Sal - va,
Save Thou me, Oh save,
C.
fons pi - e - ta - - - - - - - tis!
Oh fount of mer - - - - - - cy!
T.
fons pi - e - ta - tis! Sal - va,
Oh fount of mer - cy! Save me,
B.
fons pi - e - ta - tis! Sal - va me, Sal - va
Oh fount of mer - cy! Save Thou me, Save Thou
sempre animando
f

allarg. stent.
L
31
a tempo
SOP.
Sal - - va me,
Save Thou me,
MEZZO-SOP.
- ta - - - - - tis!
mer - - - - - cy!
TEN.
Sal - va, Sal - va me,
Oh save, Save Thou me,
BASS
dolce
pp a tempo
me, Sal - - va me, Sal - va me,
me, Save Thou me, Save Thou me,
CHORUS
S.
Sal - - va me,
Save Thou me,
C.
Sal - va, Sal - va me,
Save me, Save Thou me,
T.
Sal - va, Sal - va me,
Oh save, Save Thou me,
Save Thou me,
Sal - - va me,
B.
me, Sal - va me,
me, Save Thou me,
allarg. stent.
pp a tempo

SOP.
mf
Sal - - - - va,
Save me,
MEZZO-SOP.
mf
Sal - va me, fons pi - e -
Save Thou me, Oh fount of
TEN.
mf
Sal - - - - va,
Save me,
BASS
mf
Sal - va, me, fons pi - e -
Save Thou me, Oh fount of
Save me, Save me,
Sal - va, Sal - - va,
S.
pp 2nd SOPS.
1st SOPS.
mf
Sal - va me, Sal - - - - va,
Save Thou me, Save me,
C.
pp 2nd CONTRALTOS
1st CONTRALTOS
mf
Sal - va me! Sal - va me, Sal - - - - va,
Save Thou me, Save Thou me, Save me,
CHORUS
T.
pp 1st TENORS
mf
Sal - va me, Sal - va me, fons pi - e -
Save Thou me, Save Thou me, Oh fount of
1st BASSES
B. pp
mf
Sal - va me, Sal - va me, fons pi - e -
Save Thou me, Save Thou me, Oh fount of
pp
mf

CHORUS SITS
SOP.
Sal - va me!
Save Thou me!
MEZZO-SOP.
- ta - - - tis!
mer - - cy!
TEN.
Sal - va me!
Save Thou me!
BASS
- ta - - - tis!
mer - - cy!
CHORUS
S.
Sal - va me!
Save Thou me!
C.
Sal - va me!
Save Thou me!
SIT TO P84
T.
- ta - - - tis!
mer - - cy!
B.
- ta - - - tis!
mer - - cy!
cresc.
dim. ed allarg.

MEZZO-SOP.
32 Lo stesso tempo
espress.
Re - cor - da - re, Je - su pi - e, Quod sum
Ah, re - mem - ber, gen - tle Je - sus, 'Twas for
32 Lo stesso tempo
pp
MEZZO-SOP.
cau - sa tu - æ vi - æ.
my sake Thou didst suf - fer.
SOP. cantabile
Re - cor - da - re,
Ah, re - mem - ber,
SOP.
Je - su pi - e, Quod sum cau - sa, Quod sum
gen - tle Je - sus, 'Twas for my sake Thou didst
MEZZO-SOP.
Quod sum cau - sa tu - æ
'Twas for my sake Thou didst

SOP.
33
cau - - - sa tu-æ vi-æ, Ne me
suf - - - fer, Thou didst suf-fer, On that
MEZZO-SOP.
vi - - æ, Ne me per-das il-la di-e,
suf - - fer, On that day do not for-sake me,
33
pp
m.s.
SOP.
a poco a poco animando
per-das il-la di - - - - - - e, Ne me per-das
day do not for-sake me, On that day do
MEZZO-SOP.
Ne me per - das, Ne me per-das
Ho - ly Je - sus, On that day do
m.s.
a poco a poco animando
M
34
SOP.
a tempo
il-la di - e. Quæ-rens me,
not for-sake me. Seek-ing me,
MEZZO-SOP.
il-la di - e. Quæ-rens me,
not for-sake me. Seek-ing me,
34
M
a tempo
p

SOP.
Quæ - rens me, se - di - sti las - sus, Re - de - mi - sti,
seek - ing me Thou wast af - flict - ed, To re - deem me,
MEZZO-SOP.
Quæ - rens me, se - di - sti las - sus, Re - de - mi -
seek - ing me Thou wast af - flict - ed, To re - deem
col canto
SOP.
dolciss.
p
mf
Re - de - mi - sti cru - cem pas - sus; Tan - tus
Ah, re - deem me by Thy pas - sion; Let such
MEZZO-SOP.
sti, Re - de - mi - sti cru - cem pas - sus; Tan - tus
me, Ah, re - deem me by Thy pas - sion; Let such
col canto
SOP.
la - bor non sit cas - sus. Ju - ste
la - bour not be use - less. Just and
MEZZO-SOP.
la - bor non sit cas - sus. Ju - ste
la - bour not be use - less. Just and
pp

35
SOP.
animando sempre sino alla fine
Ju - dex ul - ti - o - nis, Do - num fac
up - right Judge al - migh - ty, Grant me grace
M.-SOP.
Ju - dex ul - ti - o - nis, Do - num
up - right Judge al - migh - ty, Grant me
animando sempre sino alla fine
m.d.
re-mis-si-o - nis An - te di - em
for my a-tone - ment Ere that day come
pp
un poco animando
fac re-mis-si-o - nis An - te di - em
grace for my a-tone - ment Ere that day come
pp dolce
ra - ti - o - nis, Do
for my judg - ment, Grant
dolce
p
ra - ti - o - nis, Do
for my judg - ment, Grant

SOP.
36
animando
num fac re-mis-si - o - - - - nis An - te di - em, An - te
me grace for my a - tone - - - - ment Ere the day come, Ere the
M.-SOP.
num fac re-mis-si - o - - - - nis An - te
me grace for my a - tone - - - - ment Ere the
36
pp
pp animando
SOP.
di - em, An - te di - em,
day come, Ere the day come,
MEZZO-SOP.
di - - - - - em, An - te di - em ra - ti - o - nis, An - te
day come, Ere the day I stand be - fore Thee, Ere the
f
SOP.
An - te di - - - em ra - ti - o - nis.
Ere the day I stand be - fore Thee.
MEZZO-SOP.
di - em ra - ti - o - - - - - - nis.
day I stand be - fore Thee.
pp col canto

TENOR
In - ge - mi - sco tam-quam re - - - us: Cul - pa ru - bet vul - tus
I la - ment, for I am guilt - - y: And I blush for my wrong -
pp
TEN.
ppp
me - us: Sup - pli - can - ti, Sup - pli - can - ti par - ce De - - us.
- do - ing: I im - plore Thee, I im - plore Thee, Sa - viour, spare me.
ppp
37 Poco meno mosso
TEN.
dolce con calma
dolciss. morendo
Qui Ma - ri - am ab - sol - vi - - - - sti,
37
Thou hast dried the tears of Ma - - - - ry,
dolce
pp
TEN.
dolciss.
Et la - tro - nem e - xau - di - - - - sti, Mi - hi
And the rob - ber won Thy pi - - - - ty, So shall
p

TEN.
quo - que spem de - di - sti, Mi - - - hi quo - -
I too hope for par - don, So shall I
pp
cresc.
m.s.
TEN.
- - - que spem de - di - - - - sti.
- - - pray for thy par - - - - don.
pp
N
38
p
ppp
TEN.
Pre-ces me - æ non sunt di - gnæ, Sed tu
My pe - ti - tions are un-wor - thy, Yet have
TEN.
bo - nus fac be - ni - gne, Ne pe-ren - ni cre-mer
mer - cy, do not send me To the fire flam - ing for
m.s.

39 O
TEN.
i - - - - - gne.
e - - - - - ver.
espress.
TEN. dolce
In - ter — o - ves lo - cum præ - sta, Et ab hæ - dis me — se -
In — Thy sheep-fold let me en - ter, Do not herd me with the
TEN.
- ques - tra, In - ter o - ves lo - cum
guilt - y, In Thy sheep - fold let me
p
TEN.
præ - sta, Et ab hæ - dis me se - que - - - -
en - ter, Do not herd me with the guilt - - - -

40
a tempo
TEN.
animando
- stra Sta - tu - ens, Sta - - tu -
- y, Set me there, set me
pp animando
ppp
f a tempo
ens in par - te dex - - - -
there up - on Thy right
morendo
pp
- tra, Et ab hæ - dis me se -
hand, Do not herd me with the
ppp con espress.
ques - tra, Sta - tu - ens in par - te dex - - - - tra.
guilt - y, Set me there up - on Thy right hand.
f

41
Andante (♩ = 96)
con forza
BASS
Con - fu - ta - tis ma - le - dic - tis,
When the cur - sèd all are ban - ished,
41
ff
f
poco accelerando
BASS
Flam - mis a - cri - bus ad - dic - tis, Vo - ca me cum be - ne -
Doomed to that de - vour - ing fur - nace, Sum - mon me a - mong the
p dolce
f
pp
BASS
- dic - tis.
bless - ed.
cantabile
O - ro sup - plex et ac -
On my knees I fall be -
pp
BASS
42
- cli - nis, Cor con - tri - tum qua - si ci - nis,
- fore Thee, Sor - row turns my heart to ash - es,
42

BASS
Ge - re cu - ram me - i fi - nis. O - ro sup - plex et ac -
Grant me grace at my de - part - ing. On my knees I fall be -
p
BASS
p
rall.
f
- cli - nis, Cor con - tri - tum qua - si ci - nis, Ge - re,
- fore Thee, Sor - row turns my heart to ash - es, Grant me,
p
rall.
f
BASS
Ge - re cu - ram me - i fi - nis.
grant me com - fort at my last hour.
P
43
BASS
ff
Con - fu - ta - tis ma - le - dic - tis,
When the cur - sèd all are ban - ished,
43
P
mf
ff

SOP.
pp
Sal - va me, fons pi-e - ta - tis!
Save Thou me, Fount of com - pas - sion!
MEZZO-SOP.
me, Sal - va me, fons pi - e -
me, Save Thou me, Fount of com-
TEN.
BASS
CHORUS
S.
ppp
Sal - va me, Sal - va me,
Save Thou me, Save Thou me,
C.
ppp
Sal - va me, Sal - va me,
Save Thou me, Save Thou me,
T.
ppp
Sal - va me, Sal - va me,
Save Thou me, Save Thou me,
B.
ppp
Sal - va me, Sal - va me,
Save Thou me, Save Thou me,

BASS
Flam - mis a - cri - bus ad - dic - - - - tis,
Doomed to that de - vour - ing fur - - - - nace,
mf
ff
dolce cantabile
BASS
p
Vo - ca me cum be - ne - dic - tis,
Sum - mon me a - mong the bless - ed,
espress.
p
BASS
f
Vo - ca me cum be - ne - dic - tis, Vo - ca me,
Sum - mon me a - mong the bless - ed, Sum - mon me,
p
f
BASS
Vo - ca me cum be - ne - dic - tis.
Sum - mon me a - mong the bless - ed.
f
pp

44
Q
BASS
O - ro sup - plex et ac - cli - nis, Cor con
On my knees I fall be - fore Thee, Sor - row
pp
BASS
- tri - tum qua - si ci - nis, Ge - re cu - ram me - i
turns my heart to ash - es, Grant me grace at my de -
45
BASS
p
fi - nis, O - ro sup - plex et ac - cli - nis, Cor con - tri - tum qua - si ci - nis,
- part - ing, On my knees I fall be - fore Thee, Sor - row turns my heart to ash - es,
p
p
BASS
f
Ge - re, Ge - re cu - ram me - i fi - nis, Ge - -
Grant me, grant me com - fort at my dy - ing, Grant
f

BASS
re, Ge - re cu - ram me - i fi -
me, grant me com - fort when my hour
pp
f
R
46
STAND
-nis,
comes.
O - ro
On my
poco rall.
sup - plex et ac - cli - nis, Ge - re cu - ram,
knees I fall be - fore Thee, Grant me com - fort,
CHORUS RISES
47
Allegro come prima
ten.
Ge - re cu - ram me - i fi - nis.
grant me com - fort at my last hour.
ff

S.
C.
T.
B.
CHORUS
ff
an - - -
i - - -
Di - - es
Day of
Di - es i - ræ, Di - es i - - ræ,
Day of an - ger, Day of an - - ger,
Di - es i - ræ, Di - es i - - -
Day of an - ger, Day of an - - -
i - - - - - - - - - - - - - ræ,
an - - - - - - - - - - - - - ger,
Di - es i - - - - - - - - - - ræ,
Day of an - - - - - - - - - - ger,
8
3

48
T.
ff
Di - es il - la, di - es
Day of ter - ror, Day of
B.
ff
Di - es il - la, di - es
Day of ter - ror, Day of
CHORUS
48
S.
ff
ter
il
Di - - es il
Day - - of ter
C.
ff
ter
il
Di - - es il
Day - - of ter
T.
ter
il
il - - la, Di - es il
ter - - ror Day of ter
B.
il
ter
CHORUS

CHORUS
S.
- ror,
- la,
- la, Sol - vet
- ror, All shall
C.
la,
- la, Sol - vet
- ror, All shall
T.
- la, Sol - vet,
- ror, All shall
B.
- la, Sol - - vet,
- ror, All shall
S.
sæ - clum in fa - vil - la,
crum - ble in - to ash - es,
C.
sæ - clum in fa - vil - la,
crum - ble in - to ash - es,
T.
sol - vet sæ - clum in fa - vil - la,
crum - ble, crum - ble in - to ash - es,
B.
Sol - - vet sæ - clum in fa - vil - la,
crum - - ble, crum - ble in - to ash - es,

S.
Te - ste Da - vid cum Si - byl - la,
This was Da - vid's re - ve - la - tion,
C.
Te - ste Da - vid cum Si - byl - la,
This was Da - vid's re - ve - la - tion,
CHORUS
T.
Te - ste Da - vid cum Si - byl - la,
This was Da - vid's re - ve - la - tion,
B.
Te - ste Da - vid cum Si - byl - la,
This was Da - vid's re - ve - la - tion,
49
ff
Di - es i - ræ, Di - es i - -
Day of an - ger, Day of an - -

S.
C.
T.
B.
CHORUS
dim.
p
-ræ, Di-es i - - - - - - - ræ, Di - es i-ræ, di-
-ger, Day of an - - - - - - - ger, Day of an-ger, Day
-ræ, Di - es i - ræ, di - es il-la! di-
-ger, Day of an - ger, Day of an-ger, Day
-ræ, Di - es i - ræ, di - es il - la!
-ger, Day of an - ger, Day of ter - ror!
- es il - la!
of ter - ror!
di - es il-la!
Day of ter-ror!
morendo

MEZZO-SOP.
con molto espressione
50 Largo (♩ = 60)
La - cry - mo - sa di - es__ il - la, Qua re - sur - get ex fa -
Day of bit - ter la - men - ta - tion. When man ri - ses up from
50 Largo (♩ = 60)
lunghe e lamentose
p
MEZZO-SOP.
vil - la, Ju - di - can - dus ho - mo re - us. Hu - ic__ er - go par - ce De - -
ash - es, Doomed to judg - ment, Lost and guilt - y, Then, Lord, pi - ty this Thy ser - -
MEZZO-SOP.
piangente
- us: La - cry - mo - sa,__ La - cry-
- vant: Sigh - ing,__ weep ing,__ sigh - ing,__
Cantabile
BASS
La - cry - mo - sa di - es__ il - la, Qua re - sur - get ex fa -
Day of bit - ter la - men - ta - tion, When man ri - ses up from
come un lamento

MEZZO-SOP.
- - mo - sa di - es il - la, di - es il -
weep - ing, Day of bit - ter la - men - ta -
f
BASS
- vil - la, Ju - di - can - dus ho - mo re - us, Hu - ic er - go par - ce De -
ash - es, Doomed to judg - ment, Lost and guilt - y, Then, Lord, pi - ty this Thy ser -
S
51
SOP.
pp
dolciss.
Hu - ic er - - - go par - ce
Lord, have mer - - - cy, mer - cy
MEZZO-SOP.
ppp
la. Hu - ic er - go par - ce De - us,
- tion. Lord, have mer - cy on Thy ser - vant,
BASS
us.
- vant.
CHORUS
S.
pp
Hu - ic er - go par - ce De - us, par - ce
Lord, have mer - cy on Thy ser - vant, Lord, have
C.
pp
Hu - ic er - go par - ce De - us, par - ce
Lord, have mer - cy on Thy ser - vant, Lord, have
pp leggiero

SOP.
lamentoso
De - - - - us. La - - - cry - -
on him. Sigh - ing,
MEZZO-SOP.
par - ce De - us. La - - - cry -
mer - cy on him. Day of
TEN.
p Cantabile
La - cry - mo - sa di - es
Day of bit - ter la - men -
BASS
Cantabile
p
La - cry - mo - sa di - es
Day of bit - ter la - men -
S.
Cantabile
par - ce De - - us. La - cry -
mer - cy on him. Day of
C.
Cantabile
par - ce De - - us. La - cry -
mer - cy on him. Day of
CHORUS
T.
Cantabile
p
La - cry - mo - sa di - es
Day of bit - ter la - men -
Cantabile
B.
p
La - cry - mo - sa di - es
Day of bit - ter la - men -
con espress.
cantabile

SOP.
- mo - sa, La - cry - mo - sa
weep - ing, sigh - ing, weep - ing,
MEZZO-SOP.
- mo - sa di - es il - la, Qua re - sur - get ex fa - vil - la,
bit - ter la - men - ta - tion, When man shall rise up from ash - es,
TEN.
il - la, Qua re - sur - get ex fa - vil - la, Ju - di -
- ta - tion, When man ri - ses up from ash - es, Doomed to
BASS
il - la, Qua re - sur - get ex fa - vil - la, Ju - di -
- ta - tion, When man ri - ses up from ash - es, Doomed to
CHORUS
S.
- mo - sa di - es il - la, Qua re - sur - get ex fa - vil - la,
bit - ter la - men - ta - tion, When man shall rise up from ash - es,
C.
- mo - sa di - es il - la, Qua - re - sur - get ex fa - vil - la,
bit - ter la - men - ta - tion, When man shall rise up from ash - es,
T.
il - la, Qua re - sur - get ex fa - vil - la, Ju - di -
- ta - tion, When man ri - ses up from ash - es, Doomed to
B.
il - la, Qua re - sur - get ex fa - vil - la, Ju - di -
- ta - tion, When man ri - ses up from ash - es, Doomed to

SOP.
di - es, di - es il - la, La - cry - mo - - - - -
bit - ter, bit - ter sor - row, bit - ter sor - - - - -
MEZZO-SOP.
Ju - di - can - dus ho - mo re - us, Ju - di - can-dus ho - mo re - -
Doomed to judg-ment, Lost and guilt - y, Then, Lord, pi - ty this Thy ser - -
TEN.
- can - dus ho - mo re - us, Hu - ic er - go par - ce De - -
judg - ment, Lost and guilt - y, Then, Lord, pi - ty this Thy ser - -
BASS
- can - dus ho - mo re - us, Hu - ic er - go par - ce De - -
judg - ment, Lost and guilt - y, Then, Lord, pi - ty this Thy ser - -
CHORUS
S.
Ju - di - can - dus ho - mo re - us, Hu - ic er - go par - ce De - -
Doomed to judg-ment, Lost and guilt - y, Then, Lord, pi - ty this Thy ser - -
C.
Ju - di - can - dus ho - mo re - us, Hu - ic er - go par - ce De - -
Doomed to judg-ment, Lost and guilt - y, Then, Lord, pi - ty this Thy ser - -
T.
- can - dus ho - mo re - us. Hu - ic er - go par - ce De - -
judg - ment, Lost and guilt - y, Then, Lord, pi - ty this Thy ser - -
B.
- can - dus ho - mo re - us, Hu - ic er - go par - ce De - -
judg - ment, Lost and guilt - y, Then, Lord, pi - ty this Thy ser - -

52
SOP.
dolciss.
- sa,
La - cry - mo - sa di - - - -
- row,
Day of bit - ter, bit - - - -
MEZZO-SOP.
ppp
- us, Hu - - - - - - - ic er - go par - - - -
- vant, Then, Lord, pi - ty and
TEN.
- us,
- vant,
BASS
- us,
- vant,
S.
sotto voce
ppp Cantabile
- us, Hu - ic er - go par - ce De - us, par - ce
- vant, Then, Lord, pi - ty this Thy ser - vant, and in
C.
ppp
- us, Hu - ic er - go par - ce De - us, par - ce
- vant, Then, Lord, pi - ty this Thy ser - vant, and in
CHORUS
T.
- us,
- vant,
B.
- us,
- vant,
52
ppp dolce

SOP.
animando un poco
es, di - es il - la!
ter la - men - ta - tion!
MEZZO-SOP.
ce De - us,
spare Thou him.
TEN.
BASS
CHORUS
S.
animando un poco
p
par - ce De - us, Hu - ic
mer - cy spare him. Lord, have
C.
p
par - ce, De - us, Hu - ic er-go,
mer - cy, spare him. Lord, have pi-ty,
T.
2nd TENORS
1st TEN.
p
Hu - ic er-go par - ce De-us,
Lord, have pi-ty on Thy ser-vant,
B.
2nd BASSES
1st BASSES
p
Hu - ic er-go par - ce De-us,
Lord, have pi-ty on Thy ser-vant,
8
animando un poco
m.d.
p
cresc.

Come prima
SOP.
Hu - ic er - go par - ce
Lord, have mer - cy then, Lord,
MEZZO-SOP.
par - ce, par - ce De - us, par - ce,
Lord, in mer - cy spare him, Lord, in
TEN.
Hu - ic er - go par - ce,
Then have pi - ty, Lord, in
BASS
Hu - ic er - go par - ce De - us, Hu - ic
Pi - ty him then, Lord, and spare him, On that
Come prima
CHORUS
S.
er - go par - ce De - us, par - ce,
pi - ty, spare Thy ser - vant, Lord, in
C.
Hu - ic er - go, par
Lord, have pi - ty, Spare
T.
pp
Hu - ic er - go par - ce,
Then have pi - ty, Lord, in
B.
pp
Hu - ic er - go par - ce De - us, Hu - ic
Pi - ty him then, Lord, and spare him, On that
Come prima

T
53
SOP.
dolciss.
pp
De - us: Pi - e Je - su, Do - mi - ne, Do - na
spare him. Bless - ed Je - sus, Christ Our Lord, Sa - viour,
MEZZO-SOP.
f
par - ce De - us: Pi - e Je - su, Do - mi - ne, Do - na
mer - cy spare him. Bless - ed Je - sus, Christ Our Lord, Sa - viour,
TEN.
pp dolciss.
par - ce De - us: Je - su, Do - na
mer - cy spare him. Je - sus, Sa - viour,
BASS
pp dolciss.
er - go par - ce De - us: Do - na
day, in mer - cy spare him. Sa - viour,
CHORUS
S.
par - ce De - us:
mer - cy spare him.
C.
- - ce De - us:
him, spare him.
T.
par - ce De - us:
mer - cy spare him.
B.
er - go par - ce De - us:
day, in mer - cy spare him.
pp dolciss.

SOP.
e - is re - qui - em, Pi - e Je - su, Do - mi - ne,
grant them rest and peace, Bless - ed Je - sus, Christ Our Lord,
MEZZO-SOP.
e - is re - qui - em, Pi - e Je - su, Do - mi - ne, Do - na
grant them rest and peace, Bless - ed Je - sus, Christ Our Lord, Sa - viour
TEN.
e - is re - qui - em, Pi - e Je - su, Do - mi - ne, Do - na
grant them rest and peace, Bless - ed Je - sus, Christ Our Lord, Sa - viour
BASS
e - is re - qui - em, Pi - e Je - su, Do - mi - ne,
grant them rest and peace, Bless - ed Je - sus, Christ Our Lord,
SOP.
Do - - - - - na, e - is re - qui -
Grant them, grant them rest and
MEZZO-SOP.
e - is, Do - na e - is re - qui -
grant them, Sa - viour, grant them rest and
TEN.
e - is, Do - na e - is re - qui -
grant them, Sa - viour, grant them rest and
BASS
Do - na e - is, Do - na re - - qui -
Grant them Thy rest and peace, rest and
p

U
54
SOP.
allarg. e dolce
pp
- em,
peace.
Pi - e, Pi - e Je -
Bless - ed, bless - ed Lord,
MEZZO-SOP.
pp
- em,
peace.
Pi - e Je - su,
Bless - ed Je - sus,
TEN.
pp
- em,
peace.
Pi - e Je - su,
Bless - ed Je - sus,
BASS
pp
- em,
peace.
Pi - e Je - su,
Bless - ed Je - sus,
CHORUS
S.
pp
Pi - e Je - su,
Bless - ed Je - su,
C.
pp
Pi - e Je - su,
Bless - ed Je - su,
T.
pp
Pi - e Je - su, Do - mi - ne,
Bless - ed Je - sus, Christ Our Lord,
Bless - ed Je - su Christ Our Lord,
Pi - e Je - su, Do - mi - ne,
B.
pp
Pi - e Je - su,
Bless - ed Je - su
U
54
pp
m.d.
p allarg. e dolce

SOP.
(in tempo)
- su, Do - na e - is re - qui - em,
Christ, Sa - viour, grant them rest and peace.
MEZZO-SOP.
Do - na e - is re - qui - em,
Sa - viour, grant them rest and peace.
TEN.
Do - na e - is re - qui - em,
Sa - viour, grant them rest and peace.
BASS
pp
Do - na e - is re - qui - em, Pi - e
Sa - viour, grant them rest and peace. Bless - ed
CHORUS
S.
mf
Do - na e - is re - qui - em, re - qui - em,
Oh Sa-viour, grant them rest and peace, rest and peace.
C.
mf
Do - na e - is re - qui - em, re - qui - em,
Oh Sa-viour, grant them rest and peace, rest and peace.
T.
mf
Do - na e - is re - qui - em, Do - na e - is,
Oh Sa-viour, grant them rest and peace, grant them Thy peace.
B.
mf
pp
Do - na e - is re - qui - em, Do - na e - is, Pi - e
Oh Sa-viour, grant them rest and peace, grant them Thy peace. Bless - ed
mf
(in tempo)
p
pp e legato

SOP.
pp dolcissimo
re - qui - em, re - qui -
Rest and peace, rest and
MEZZO-SOP.
pp
re - qui - em, re - qui -
Rest and peace, rest and
TEN.
dolce
pp
Do - na e - is, e - is re - qui -
Sa - viour, grant them, grant them rest and
BASS
Je - su, Do - mi - ne, Do - na e - is re - qui -
Je - sus, Christ Our Lord, Sa - viour, grant them rest and
CHORUS
S.
pp dolcissimo
re - qui - em, re - qui -
rest and peace, rest and
C.
pp
re - qui - em, re qui
rest and peace, rest and
T.
pp dolce
Do - na e - is, e - is re - qui -
Grant them Thy peace, grant them Thy
B.
Je - su, Do - mi - ne, Do - na e - is re - qui -
Je - sus, Christ Our Lord, Sa - viour, grant them rest and

SOP.
55
pp
ancora più pp
- em, re - qui - em, re - qui -
peace, rest and peace, rest and
MEZZO-SOP.
TEN.
BASS
S.
C.
T.
B.
CHORUS
ancora più p

SOP.
calando
morendo ed allarg.
- em, Do - na e - is re - qui -
peace, Sa - viour, grant them rest and
MEZZO-SOP.
- em, Do - na e - is re - qui -
peace, Sa - viour, grant them rest and
TEN.
- em, Do - na e - is re - qui -
peace, Sa - viour, grant them rest and
BASS
- em, Do - na e - is re - qui - em, Do - na e - is re - qui -
peace, Sa - viour, grant them rest and peace, Sa - viour, grant them rest and
CHORUS
S.
calando
morendo ed allarg.
- em, Do - na e - is re - qui -
peace, Sa - viour, grant them rest and
C.
- em, Do - na e - is re - qui -
peace, Sa - viour, grant them rest and
T.
- em, Do - na e - is re - qui -
peace, Sa - viour, grant them rest and
B.
- em, Do - na e - is re - qui -
peace, Sa - viour, grant them rest and
morendo ed allarg.

SOP.
(in tempo)
ppp f
- em. A - men.
peace. A - men.
MEZZO-SOP.
ppp f
- em. A - men
peace. A - men.
TEN.
ppp f
- em. A - men.
peace. A - men.
BASS
ppp f
- em. A - men.
peace. A - men.
CHORUS
S.
p f
- em. A - men.
peace. A - men.
C.
p f
- em. A - men.
peace. A - men.
T.
ppp f
- em. A - men.
peace. A - men.
B.
ppp f
- em. A - men.
peace. A - men.
ppp (in tempo)
pp
CHORUS SITS

No. 3. DOMINE JESU

(Lord of Lords)

Soprano, Mezzo-Soprano, Tenor and Bass

CHORUS SEATED

MEZZO-SOP.
cresc.
- mi - ne Je - su Chris - te, Je - su Chris - te, Rex
- sus, Our Lord and Sa - viour, Je - sus Christ, King of
TEN.
cresc.
- mi - ne Je - su Chris - te, Je - su Chris - te, Rex
- sus, Our Lord and Sa - viour, Je - sus Christ, King of
più marcato
p
MEZZO-SOP.
f
dim.
dolciss.
A
57
glo - - - ri - æ, Rex glo - ri æ,
Kings, and King of Glo - ry,
TEN.
f
glo - - - ri - æ, Rex glo - - ri - æ,
Kings, and King, King of Glo - - - - - - ry,
57
A
f
dim.
ppp
MEZZO-SOP.
espress.
li - be - ra, li - be - ra
Set them, Oh, set them at
TEN.
li - be - ra
Set them at
cantabile
BASS
li - be - ra a - ni - mas
Set free de - part - ed souls;
p cantabile

SOP.
MEZZO-SOP.
a - ni-mas om - ni-um fi-
li - ber-ty, souls of all the
TEN.
a - ni-mas om - ni-um fi-
li - ber-ty, souls of all the
BASS
om - ni - um fi - de - li-um de-func - to - rum
free the souls of all the faith-ful de - part - ed

SOP.
MEZZO-SOP.
-de - li-um de - func - to - rum de
faith-ful who are de - part - ed from
TEN.
-de - li-um de - func - to - rum de
faith-ful who are de - part - ed from
BASS
de pœ - nis in - fer - ni,
from Hell and its tor - ments,

SOP.
MEZZO-SOP.
pœ - nis in - fer - ni et de pro - fun - do
Hell and its tor - ments, and from the sound - less
TEN.
pœ - nis in - fer - ni et de pro - fun - do
Hell and its tor - ments, and from the sound - less
BASS
et de pro - fun - do la - - - - cu:
and from the sound - less cha - - - - sm:
B
58
SOP.
MEZZO-SOP.
la - cu: de o - - re le -
cha - sm: and from the mouth of the
TEN.
la - cu: li - be - ra e - - - as de o - -
cha - sm: Oh Lord, de - li - - - ver them all
BASS
li - be - ra e - - - as de o - re le -
Oh Lord, de - li - ver them from the mouth of the
B
58
mf
f

SOP.
MEZZO-SOP.
-o - - - - - nis, ne ab-
li - - - - - on, that they
TEN.
- re le-o - nis, ne ab-sor- -
from the li - on, that they may
BASS
f
-o - - - nis, ne ab-sor - be-at e - - - - -
li - - - on, that they may not be swal - - - -
p
SOP.
MEZZO-SOP.
dim.
-sor - - be-at e - - - as, e-as tar - ta-rus,
may not be swal - - - lowed, swal-lowed up by Hell,
TEN.
- be-at e - as, ne ab-sor-be-at e - as tar - ta-rus,
not be swal - lowed, that they may not be swal - lowed up by Hell,
BASS
p
- - - as, tar - - - - - ta - - - - - rus, ne
- - - lowed, up by Hell, and
dim. sempre
pp
p

59 C
SOP.
pp
sed
but
MEZZO-SOP.
p
dim. sempre
ne ca-dant, in ob-scu-rum:
and pe-rish in its dark-ness:
TEN.
p
dim. sempre
ne ca-dant, in ob-scu-rum:
and pe-rish in its dark-ness:
BASS
più piano
dim. sempre
ca - - dant, ne ca - dant in ob - scu-rum:
pe - - rish, and pe - rish in its dark-ness:
59 C
p
ancora più piano
SOP.
cresc. sempre
portando la voce
cantabile
cresc. sempre
pp leggiero
SOP.
ppp
cantabile
dolciss.
si - gni - fer sanc - tus
let Mi - chael raise his
ppp

con più espansione
SOP.
Mi - cha - el re - præ - sen - - - -
ho - ly sign and lead them on - - - -
p
SOP.
60
pp
- tet e - - - - as in
MEZZO-SOP. - ward to Thy clear
cresc. a poco a
M. SOP.
pp
re - præ - sen - tet e - as
lead them on - ward to Thy
60
cresc. a poco a
pp
SOP.
- poco
cresc.
mf
lu - - - cem sanc - - - - - -
MEZZO-SOP. light of hea - - - - - -
cresc.
mf
in lu - - - cem sanc - - - - - -
clear light of hea - - - - - -
TEN.
p
mf
re - præ - sen - tet e - as in lu - - - - - -
lead them on - ward in - to the light
BASS
p
mf
in lu - cem sanc - - - - - -
Thy light of hea - - - - - -
- poco
cresc.
mf

SOP.
dim.
tam.
ven.
MEZZO-SOP.
dim.
tam.
ven.
TEN.
dim.
- cem sanc - tam.
of hea - ven.
BASS
dim.
p
tam, in
ven, Thy
dim.
dim.

61
Allegro mosso (♩ = 152)
SOP.
MEZZO-SOP.
TEN.
p
Quam o - lim
Of old to
BASS
poco allarg.
p
lu - cem san - ctam. Quam o - lim A - bra - hæ, Quam o - lim
light of hea - ven. Which Thou didst pro - mise of old to
Allegro mosso (♩ = 152)
61
poco allarg.
morendo
p

SOP.
mf
Quam o - lim A - - bra -
of old to A - - bra -
MEZZO-SOP.
p
Quam o - lim A - bra - hæ, Quam o - lim A - - bra -
Which Thou didst pro - - mise of old to A - bra -
TEN.
A - bra - hæ, Quam o - lim A - bra - hæ pro - mi - si - -
A - bra - ham, Which Thou didst pro - - mise, Thou didst pro - -
BASS
A - bra - hæ pro - - mi - si - sti, pro - - mi - si -
A - bra - ham un - - to A - bra - ham and his
mf
SOP.
- hæ, Quam o - lim A - bra - hæ pro - mi - si - sti et se - mi - ni e - -
- ham, As Thou didst pro - mise A - bra - ham of old to the last ge - ner - a - -
MEZZO-SOP.
- hæ,
- ham,
TEN.
- hæ,
- mise,
BASS
- sti,
seed,

SOP.
- jus.
- tion.
MEZZO-SOP.
TEN.
Quam o - lim A - bra - hæ pro - mi - si - sti et
As Thou didst pro - mise A - bra - ham of old to the
BASS
mf
SOP.
62
f
Quam o - lim A - bra -
As once of old to
MEZZO-SOP.
f
Quam o - lim A - bra - hæ
As once to A - bra - ham
TEN.
f
se - mi - ni e - - jus, Quam o - lim A - bra - hæ
last ge - ner-a - - tion. As once to A - bra - ham
BASS
f
Quam o - lim A - bra -
As once to A - bra -
62
f

SOP.
hæ pro - mi - si - sti et se - mi - ni e - -
A - bra - ham hast Thou made this pro - mise to his
MEZZO-SOP.
pro - mi - si - sti et se - mi - ni e - -
Thou hast made this pro - mise to his
TEN.
pro - mi - si - sti et se - mi - ni e - -
Thou hast spo - ken this pro - mise to his
BASS
hæ pro - mi - si - sti et se - mi - ni e - -
ham hast Thou made this pro - mise to his
SOP.
f animando
sempre dim.
63
Adagio (♩ = 66)
p
- jus, et se - mi - ni e - - - - - jus.
seed for all ge - ner - a - - - - - tions.
MEZZO-SOP.
f
sempre dim.
- jus, et se - mi - ni e - - - - - jus.
seed for all ge - ner - a - - - - - tions.
TEN.
f
sempre dim.
- jus, et se - mi - ni e - - - - - jus.
seed for all ge - ner - a - - - - - tions.
BASS
f
sempre dim.
- jus, et se - mi - ni e - - - - - jus.
seed for all ge - ner a - - - - - tions.
sempre dim.
63
Adagio (♩ = 66)
f animando
dim.
p ppp

Calmo—Lento le semicrome
dolciss.
TEN.
Ho - sti - as et pre - ces ti - bi,
Sa - cri - fice and prayers, Oh Lord, we
TEN.
animando un poco
Do - mi - ne, ti - bi, Do - mi - ne, lau - dis of - fe - ri -
of - fer Thee, Hear our prayers, Oh Lord, of - fered with songs of
animando un poco
pp
pp
D
64
SOP.
dolciss.
Ho - sti - as et pre - ces
Prayers and sa - cri - fi - ces,
MEZZO-SOP.
dolciss.
Ho - sti - as et pre - ces
Prayers and sa - cri - fi - ces,
TEN.
- mus.
praise.
BASS
dolciss.
ten.
Ho - sti - as et pre - ces
Sa - cri - fice and prayers, Oh
D
64
ppp
ppp dolciss.

SOP.
ti - bi, Do - mi-ne,
Lord, we of - fer Thee,
MEZZO-SOP.
ti - bi, Do - mi-ne,
Lord, we of - fer Thee,
TEN.
BASS
ti - bi, Do - mi - ne, ti - bi, Do - mi -
Lord, we of - fer Thee; Hear our prayers, Oh
ppp
SOP.
65
lau - dis of - fe - ri-mus,
min - gled with songs of praise,
MEZZO-SOP.
lau - dis of - fe - ri-mus,
min - gled with songs of praise,
TEN.
tu su - sci-pe pro
Do Thou re-ceive them
BASS
tr
- ne, lau - dis of - fe - ri - mus,
Lord, of - fered with songs of praise,
65
p
pp

SOP.
pp
lau - dis of - fe - - - - - - - ri -
of - fered with songs of
MEZZO-SOP.
pp
lau - dis of - fe - - ri - mus, lau - -
of - fered with songs of praise, of
TEN.
pp
a - ni - ma - bus il - lis, qua - rum ho - di - e me-mo - ri - am
for those souls de - part - ed, for those souls whom we this day here com-
BASS
pp
lau - - - dis of
Hear, Lord, our
p
SOP.
ppp
- mus, lau - - - dis;
praise; Prai - - - ses;
MEZZO-SOP.
ppp
- dis of - fe - ri - mus, lau - - - dis;
praise, with songs of praise; Prai - - - ses;
TEN.
fa - ci - mus: fac e - as, Do - mi-ne, de mor - - te tran-
mem - or - ate: Grant them, Oh Lord, to pass, from death in - to
BASS
ppp
- fe - ri - mus, lau - - - dis;
songs of praise. Prai - - - ses;
p dim.
ppp
m.s.

66 E
con espress.
SOP.
MEZZO-SOP.
TEN.
BASS
fac e - as, Do - mi-ne,
Grant them, Oh Lord, to pass,
pp
fac e - as
Grant them, Oh
tr
- si - re ad vi - tam,
life e - ver - last - ing,
fac e - as
Grant them, Oh
fac e - as,
Grant them, Oh
pp
sempre pianissimo
p
fac e - as, Do - mi-ne,
Grant them, Oh Lord, to pass,
cresc.
de mor - - -
from death
Do - mi-ne, fac e - as, Do - mi - ne, de mor - te
Lord, to pass, Grant them, Oh Lord, to pass from death in -
Do - mi-ne, fac e - as, Do - mi - ne, de
Lord, to pass, Grant them, Oh Lord, to pass from
Do - mi-ne, fac e - as Do - mi - ne, de
Lord, to pass, Grant them, Oh Lord, to pass from

SOP.
pp
tr.
sotto voce parlando
te— tran- si- re ad vi - - - - tam,
in - to life e-ver-last - - - - ing,
fac e - as, Do- mi- ne,
Grant them to pass, Oh Lord,
MEZZO-SOP.
pp
sotto voce parlando
— tran - si- re ad vi - - - - tam,
- to life e-ver-last - - - - ing,
fac e - as, Do - mi - ne,
Grant them to pass, Oh Lord,
TEN.
pp
sotto voce parlando
mor- te tran-si- re ad vi - - - - tam,
death in-to life e-ver-last - - - - ing,
fac e - as, Do- mi- ne,
Grant them to pass, Oh Lord,
BASS
pp
pp sotto voce parlando
mor - te tran si - - re ad vi - tam,
death in-to life e-ver-last - ing,
fac e - as
Grant them to
p
ppp
pp espress.
SOP.
67
morendo
Come prima
fac e - as de mor- te
from death in-to liv-ing,
tran - sire ad vi - tam.
life e-ver-last - ing.
MEZZO-SOP.
morendo
fac e - as de mor- te
from death in-to liv-ing,
tran - sire ad vi - tam.
life e-ver-last - ing.
TEN.
morendo
fac e - as de mor- te
from death in-to liv-ing,
tran - sire ad vi - tam.
life e-ver-last - ing.
BASS
f
Do- mi- ne,
pass, Oh Lord,
fac e - as de mor- te.
from death in-to liv-ing.
Quam o - lim
Which Thou didst
67
Come prima
morendo
f

SOP.
MEZZO-SOP.
f
Quam o - lim A - bra -
Which Thou didst pro - -
TEN.
f
Quam o lim A - bra - hæ Quam o - lim A - bra -
of old to A - bra - ham, Which Thou didst pro - -
BASS
A - bra - hæ Quam o - lim A - bra - hæ pro - - - mi -
pro - mise of old to A - bra - ham, un - to
SOP.
f
Quam o - lim A - bra - hæ, Quam o lim A - bra - hæ, pro - mi -
of old to A - bra - ham As Thou didst pro - mise A - bra - ham of
MEZZO-SOP.
- hæ, Quam o - lim A - bra - hæ,
- mise of old to A - bra - ham,
TEN.
- hæ, pro - mi - si - sti,
- mise, Thou didst pro - mise,
BASS
- si - sti, pro - mi - si - sti,
A - bra - ham, and his seed,

SOP.
-si - sti, et se-mi-ni e - jus.
old to the last ge-ner-a - tion.
MEZZO-SOP.
TEN.
Quam o-lim A-bra-
As Thou didst pro-mise
BASS
mf
SOP.
68
f
Quam
As
MEZZO-SOP.
f
Quam o - lim
As once to
TEN.
f
-hæ pro-mi - si - sti, et se-mi-ni e - jus. Quam o - lim
A-bra-ham of old to the last ge-ner-a - tion, As once to
BASS
f
Quam o - lim
As once to
68
3
f

SOP.
o - lim A - bra - hæ pro - mi - si - sti, et
once of old to A - bra - ham hast Thou made this
MEZZO-SOP.
A - bra - hæ pro - mi - si - - sti, et
A - bra - ham Thou hast made this
TEN.
A - bra - hæ pro - mi - si - sti, et
A - bra - ham Thou hast spo - ken this
BASS
A - bra - hæ pro - mi - si - sti, et
A - bra - ham hast Thou made this
SOP.
ff
se mi - ni e - jus, pro - mi - si - sti, pro - mi -
pro - mise to his seed, Thou didst pro - mise, Thou didst
MEZZO-SOP.
ff
se - mi - ni e - jus, pro - mi - si - sti, pro - mi -
pro - mise to his seed, Thou didst pro - mise, Thou didst
TEN.
ff
se - mi - ni e - jus, pro - mi - si - sti, pro - mi -
pro - mise to his seed, Thou didst pro - mise, Thou didst
BASS
ff
se - mi - ni e - jus, pro - mi - si - sti, pro - mi -
pro - mise to his seed, Thou didst pro - mise, Thou didst
ff
m.s.
m.s.

SOP.
- si - sti, pro - mi - si - sti, A - - - - - - bra - -
pro - mise, Thou didst pro - mise A - - - - - - bra - -
MEZZO-SOP.
- si - sti, pro - mi - si - sti, A - - - - - - bra - -
pro - mise, Thou didst pro - mise A - - - - - - bra - -
TEN.
- si - sti, pro - mi - si - sti, A - - - - - - bra - -
pro - mise, Thou didst pro - mise A - - - - - - bra - -
BASS
- si - sti, pro - mi - si - sti, A - bra - hæ
pro - mise, Thou didst pro - mise A - bra - ham
m.s.
8
SOP.
dim.
p
hæ et se - - - - - - mi - ni
ham for all ge - ner -
MEZZO-SOP.
dim.
p
hæ et se - - - - - - mi - ni
ham for all ge - ner -
TEN.
dim.
p
hæ et se - - - - - - mi - ni
ham for all ge - ner -
BASS
dim.
p
pro - mi - si - sti se - - - - - - mi - ni
Thou didst pro - mise all ge - ner -
dim.
p

SOP.
MEZZO-SOP.
TEN.
BASS
69
Come prima
ben legato
pp
e - - - - - - - jus. Li - be - ra
a - - - - - - - tions. Oh Lord, de -
ppp
p
a - ni mas om - ni - um fi - de - li - um de - func - to - rum de
liv - er the souls of all the faith - ful de - part - ed from
dim. ppp

SOP.
morendo
leg. e dolciss.
pœ - nis in - fer - - ni,
fac e - as de
Hell and the dark pit,
to pass out of
MEZZO-SOP.
morendo
pœ - nis in - fer - - ni,
Hell and the dark pit,
TEN.
morendo
pœ - nis in - fer - - ni,
Hell and the dark pit,
BASS
morendo
pœ - nis in - fer - - ni,
Hell and the dark pit,
ppp
morendo
SOP.
mor - te tran - si - re ad vi
death in - to life e - ver - last
MEZZO-SOP.
dolce
fac e - as, de mor - te tran - si - re ad vi
to pass out of death in - to life e - ver last
TEN.
dolce
fac e - as de mor - te tran - si - re ad vi
to pass out of death in - to life e - ver - last
BASS
dolce
fac e - as de mor - te tran - si - re ad vi
to pass out of death in - to life e - ver - last

SOP.
70
- tam.
- ing.
MEZZO-SOP.
- tam.
- ing
TEN.
- tam.
- ing.
BASS
- tam.
- ing.
70
pp
p
dolciss.
ppp
poco rall. e morendo
CHORUS RISES

No. 4. SANCTUS

(Holy, holy)

Fugue for Two Choirs

CHORUS 1
S.
ff
Sanc - - - - - tus!
Ho - - - - - ly!
C.
ff
Sanc - - - - - tus!
Ho - - - - - ly!
T.
ff
Sanc - - - - - tus!
Ho - - - - - ly!
B.
ff
Sanc - - - - - tus!
Ho - - - - - ly!
CHORUS 2
S.
ff
Sanc - - - - - tus!
Ho - - - - - ly!
C.
ff
Sanc - - - - - tus!
Ho - - - - - ly!
T.
ff
- tus, Sanc - - - - - tus!
- ly, Ho - - - - - ly!
B.
ff
- tus, Sanc - - - - - tus!
- ly, Ho - - - - - ly!
ff

71
Allegro (𝅗𝅥 = 112)
SOP.
CHORUS 1
mf
Sanc - tus, sanc - tus, sanc - tus, Do - mi - nus De - us Sa - ba - oth,
Ho - ly, ho - ly, ho - ly, Lord God, Lord God of Sa - ba - oth,
CONT.
mf
Sanc - tus, sanc - tus,
Ho - ly, ho - ly,
SOP. (CHORUS 2)
p
Sanc - tus, sanc - tus, sanc - tus, Do
Ho - ly, ho - ly, ho - ly, ho
71
Allegro (𝅗𝅥 = 112)
mf
SOP.
Ple - ni sunt cœ - li et ter - ra glo
Earth and Hea - ven are full of ech - oes
CONT.
sanc - tus, Do - mi - nus De - us Sa - ba - oth, Ple - ni
ho - ly, Lord God, Lord God of Sa - ba - oth, Earth and
TEN.
mf
Sanc - tus, sanc - tus, sanc - tus,
Ho - ly, ho - ly, ho - ly,
SOP.
mi - nus De - us Sa - ba - oth,
ly, Lord God of Sa - ba - oth,
CONT.
CHORUS 2
p
Sanc - tus, sanc - tus, sanc - tus, Do - mi -
Ho - ly, ho - ly, ho - ly, ho - ly, -
TEN.
p
Sanc - tus,
Ho - ly,
mf
leggiero e stacc.

S.
- - ri - a tu - a,
to Thy glo - ry,
C.
sunt cœ - li et ter - ra glo - - - - - - ri - a
Hea - ven are full of ech - oes to Thy
CHORUS 1
T.
Do - mi - nus De - us Sa - ba - oth, Ple - ni sunt cœ - li
Lord God, Lord God of Sa - ba - oth, Earth and Hea - ven are
B.
mf
Sanc - tus, sanc-tus, sanc - tus, Do - mi - nus
Ho - ly, ho - ly, ho - ly, Lord God, Lord
S.
De - us Sa - ba - oth,
God of Sa - ba - oth,
C.
- nus De - us Sa - ba - oth, De - us
Lord God of Sa - ba - oth, God of
CHORUS 2
T.
sanc - tus, sanc - tus, Do - - - - - mi - nus De - us
ho - ly, ho - ly, ho - - - - - ly, Lord God of
B.
p
San - ctus, san - ctus,
Ho - ly, ho - ly,

72
CHORUS 1
S.
Ple - ni sunt cœ - li et
All Earth and Hea - ven a -
C.
tu - a,
glo - ry,
T.
et ter - ra glo - - - - - - - ri - a tu - -
full of echoes to Thy glo - -
B.
De - us Sa - ba - oth, Ple - ni sunt cœ - li et ter -
God of Sa - ba - oth, Earth and hea - ven are full of
CHORUS 2
S.
mf
Sanc - tus, sanc - tus, sanc - tus, Do - mi - nus De - us
Ho - ly, ho - ly, ho - ly, Lord God, Lord God of
C.
Sa - ba - oth,
Sa - ba - oth,
T.
Sa - ba - oth, De - us Sa - ba -
Sa - ba - oth, God of Sa - ba -
B.
sanc - tus, Do - - - - - mi - nus De - us Sa - ba -
ho - ly, ho - - - - - ly, Lord God of Sa - ba -
72
mf

S.
ter - - - - - - ra glo - - - - ri - a tu - a.
- bove echoes to Thy glo - ry.
C.
Ple - ni sunt cœ - li et ter - ra.
All Earth and hea - ven re - ech - oes.
CHORUS 1
T.
- a.
- ry.
B.
- ra glo - - - - - - - ri - a tu - - a.
ech - oes to Thy glo - - ry.
S.
ff
Sa - ba - oth, Ple - ni sunt cœ - li et ter - ra. Ho-
Sa - ba - oth, Earth and Hea-ven are prais-ing Thee. Ho-
C.
mf
Sanc - tus, sanc-tus, sanc - tus, Do - mi - nus De - us Sa - ba-oth.
Ho - ly, ho - ly, ho - ly, Lord God, Lord God of Sa - ba-oth.
CHORUS 2
T.
ff
- oth. Ho - san - na in ex -
- oth. Ho - san - na in the
B.
ff
- oth, De - us Sa - ba - oth. Ho -
- oth, God of Sa - ba - oth. Ho -
ff

CHORUS 1
S.
ff
Ho-san - na in ex - cel - -
Ho-san - na in the high - -
C.
ff
Ho-san - na in ex -
Ho-san - na in the
T.
ff
Ho-san - na in ex - cel - sis, in ex -
Ho-san - na in the high - est, in the
B.
ff
Ho - san - na in ex -
Ho - san - na in the
CHORUS 2
S.
-san - na in ex - cel - - - - - sis.
-san - na in the high - - - - - est.
C.
ff
Ho-san - na in ex - cel - sis, Ho - san - na, Ho-
Ho-san - na in the high - est, Ho - san - na, Ho-
T.
- cel - sis, in ex - cel - sis, Ho -
high - est, in the high - est, Ho -
B.
- san - na in ex - cel - sis, Ho - san - na in ex -
- san - na in the high - est, Ho - san - na in the

S.
73
p
- - sis. Be - ne - dic - tus Be - ne -
- - est. Bless - ed is he, bless - ed
C.
p
- cel - sis. Be - ne - dic - tus qui ve - nit in no - mi - ne
high - est. Bless - ed is he that comes in the name of the
CHORUS 1
T.
- cel - sis.
high - est.
B.
- cel - sis.
high - est.
S.
p
Be - ne - dic - tus qui ve - nit in no - - - - -
Bless - ed is he that comes in the name
C.
p
- san - na. Be - ne - dic -
- san - na. Bless - ed is
CHORUS 2
T.
- san - na.
- san - na.
B.
- cel - sis.
high - est.
73
pp

S.
- dic - - tus, Be - ne - dic - tus qui
is the man, Bless - ed is___ he that
C.
Do - mi - ni, Be - ne - dic -
Lord of Lords, Bless - ed is the
CHORUS 1
T.
Be - ne - dic - tus qui ve - nit in no - mi - ne Do - mi - ni,
Bless - ed is___ he that comes in the name of the Lord of Lords,
B.
Be - ne - dic - tus,___ Be - ne - dic -
Bless - ed is the man,___ Bless - ed is_______
S.
- - mi - ne Do - - mi - ni,
- - of the Lord_______ of Lords,
C.
- tus qui ve - nit in no - - mi - ne Do - mi - ni,
he that comes in the name_______ of the Lord of Lords,
CHORUS 2
T.
B.

S.
ve - nit in no - mi - ne Do - mi - ni, Be - ne - dic - tus, Be - ne -
comes in the name of the Lord of Lords, Bless - ed, bless - ed, bless - ed,
C.
- tus qui ve - - - nit in no - mi - ne Do - mi -
- man that comes in the name of the Lord of
T.
Be - ne - dic - -
Bless - ed is the
B.
- tus, Be - ne - dic - tus, Be - ne - dic - -
he, Bless - ed is he, Bless - ed e - -
CHORUS 1
S.
Be - ne - dic - tus, Be - ne - dic -
Bless - ed is the man, Bless - ed is the
C.
Be - ne - dic - tus qui ve - nit,
Bless - ed is he that com - eth,
T.
Be - ne - dic - tus qui ve - nit in no - mi - ne Do - mi -
Bless - ed is he that comes in the name of the Lord of
B.
CHORUS 2
f
p

74
S.
-dic- tus,
bless-ed,
C.
- ni,
Lords.
Be - ne - dic
Bless - ed is
T.
- tus,
man.
B.
- tus,
- ver.
Be - ne -
Bless - ed
CHORUS 1
S.
tus, Be - ne - dic - tus, Be - ne - dic - tus,
man. Bless - ed is the man, e - ver bless - ed,
C.
Be - ne - dic - tus, que ve - nit in no - mi - ne Do - mi - ni,
Bless - ed is he that comes in the name of the Lord of Lords,
T.
- ni, Be - ne - dic - tus Be - ne - dic - tus,
Lords, Bless - ed is the man, e - ver bless - ed,
B.
Be - ne - dic - tus que ve - nit in no - mi - ne Do - mi - ni,
Bless - ed he that shall come in the name of the Lord of Lords,
CHORUS 2
74

CHORUS 1
S.
ff
Be - ne-dic - tus, Be - ne-dic-tus,
Bless - ed is the man, e - ver blessed,
C.
- tus qui ve - nit in no - mi - ne Do - mi - ni,
he that comes in the name of the Lord of Lords,
T.
ff
Be - ne-dic - tus, Be - ne-dic-tus,
Bless - ed is the man, e - ver blessed,
B.
- di - ctus qui ve - nit in no - mi - ne Do - mi - ni,
he that shall come in the name of the Lord of Lords.
CHORUS 2
S.
ff
Be - ne-dic - tus,
Bless - ed is the man,
C.
ff
Be - ne - dic - -
Bless - ed e - -
T.
ff
Be - ne-dic -
Bless - ed is,
B.
ff
Be - ne - dic - tus qui
Bless - ed e - ver, that
f

75
S.
ff
Be - ne-dic - - - - - tus,
Bless - ed is the man
C.
ff
Be - ne - dic - - tus qui ve - nit, qui ve - nit in no -
Bless - ed is he that comes, he that comes in the name
T.
ff
Be - ne-dic - tus qui ve - nit in no - mi - ne
Bless - ed is he that comes in the name of the
B.
ff
Be - ne - dic - - tus qui ve - nit in no - mi - ne
Bless - ed is he that comes in the name of the
CHORUS 1
S.
Be - ne - dic - - tus,
Bless - ed is the man
C.
- tus, Be - ne - dic - - tus qui ve - nit, qui ve - nit in no -
- ver, ev - er blest is he that comes, he that comes in the name
T.
- tus, Be - ne - dic - - tus qui ve - nit in no - mi - ne
he, ev - er blest is he that comes in the name of the
B.
ve - nit in no - mi - ne Do - mi-ni, qui ve - nit in no - mi - ne
comes in the name of the Lord of Lords, that comes in the name of the
CHORUS 2
75

CHORUS 1
S.
Be - ne - dic - tus.
Bless - ed e - ver.
C.
- mi - ne Do - mi - ni.
of the Lord of Lords.
T.
Do - mi - ni.
Lord of Lords.
B.
Do - mi - ni, in no - mi - ne.
Lord of Lords, the Lord of Lords.
CHORUS 2
S.
Be - ne - dic - tus,
Bless - ed e - ver.
C.
pp
- mi - ne Do - mi - ni, Be - ne - dic - tus,
of the Lord of Lords, Bless - ed is the man,
T.
pp
Do - mi - ni, Be - ne - dic -
Lord of Lords, Bless - ed is the
B.
dim.
pp
Do - mi - ni, in no - mi - ne, in
Lord of Lords, the Lord of Lords, in the
p

76
A
pp dolciss.
S.
Ple - ni sunt cœ - li et
Hea - ven and earth fill with
C.
Ple - ni sunt cœ - li et
Hea - ven and earth fill with
T.
Ple - ni sunt cœ - li et
Hea - ven and earth fill with
B.
Ple - ni sunt cœ - li et
Hea - ven and earth fill with
CHORUS 1
pp
Be - ne-dic - - - - tus.
Bless - ed e - - - - ver.
Be - ne - dic - tus.
Bless - ed e - ver.
- tus, Be - ne - dic - tus. Ho - san - - na,
man, bless - ed e - ver. Ho - san - - na,
no - mi - ne Do - mi - ni.
name of the Lord of Lords.
CHORUS 2
A
76
pp

S.
C.
T.
B.
CHORUS 1
ter - ra glo - - - - - - - ri - - - -
ech - oes, prais - - - - - - - ing
S.
C.
T.
B.
CHORUS 2
Ho - san - - na,
Ho - san - - na,
Ho - san - -
p

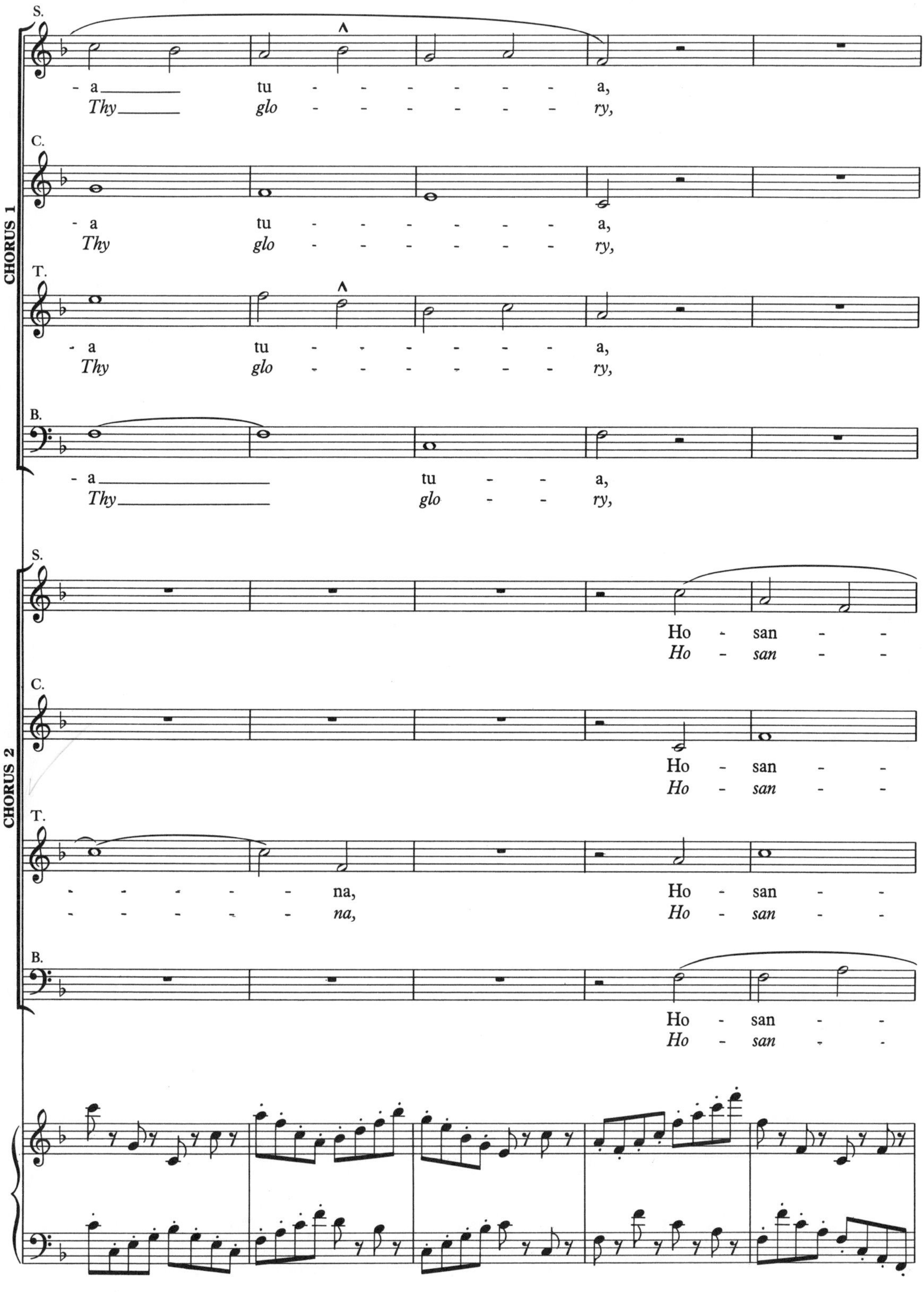
S.
C.
T.
B.
CHORUS 1
CHORUS 2
- a tu - - - - - - - a,
Thy glo - - - - - - - ry,
- a tu - - - - - - - a,
Thy glo - - - - - - - ry,
- a tu - - - - - - - a,
Thy glo - - - - - - - ry,
- a tu - - a,
Thy glo - - ry,
Ho - san - -
Ho - san - -
Ho - san - -
Ho - san - -
- - - - - na, Ho - san - -
- - - - - na, Ho - san - -
Ho - san - -
Ho - san - -

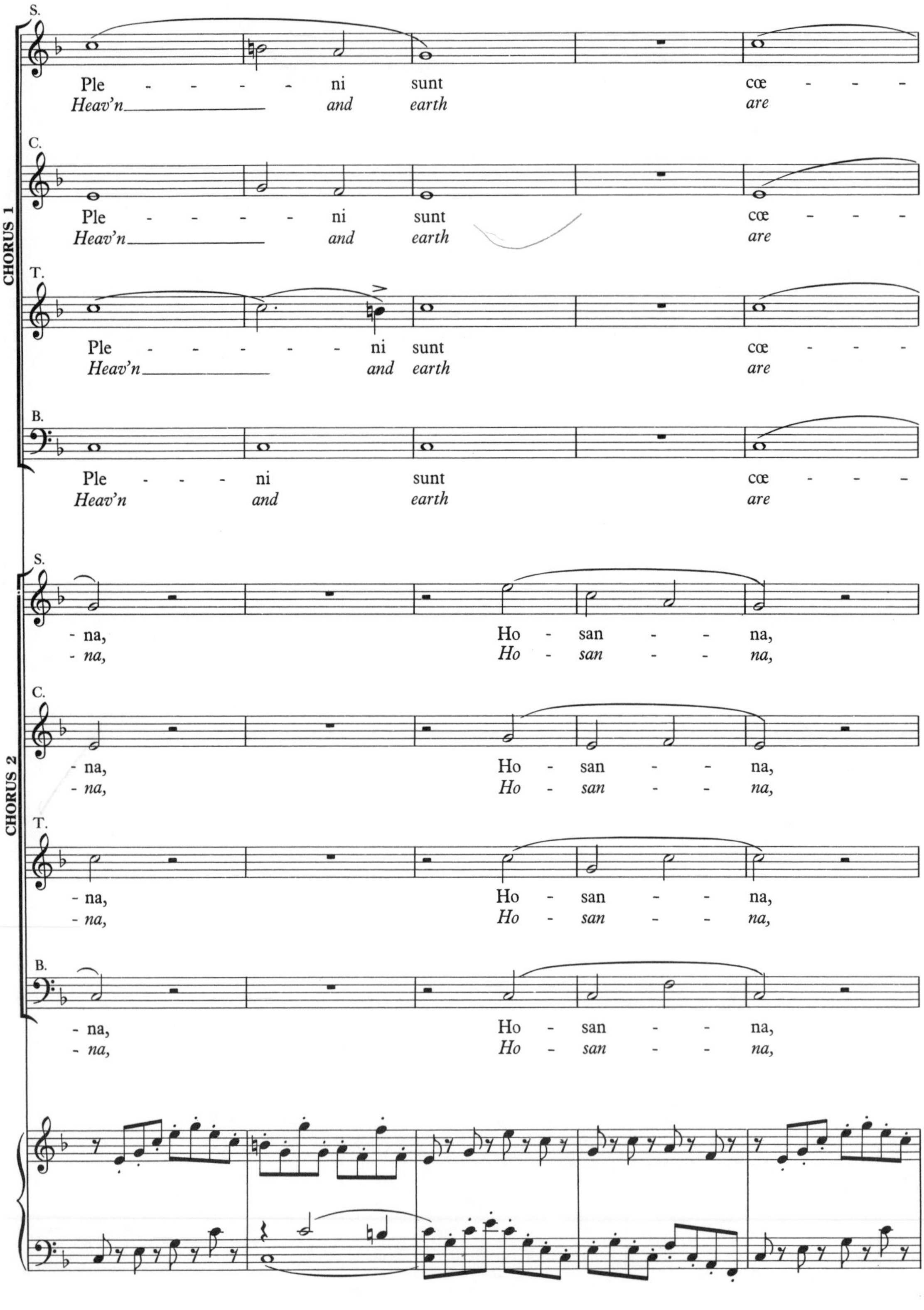
CHORUS 1
S.
Ple - - - - ni sunt cœ - - -
Heav'n and earth are
C.
Ple - - - - - ni sunt cœ - - - -
Heav'n and earth are
T.
Ple - - - - - - ni sunt cœ - - -
Heav'n and earth are
B.
Ple - - - ni sunt cœ - - -
Heav'n and earth are
CHORUS 2
S.
- na, Ho - san - - na,
- na, Ho - san - - na,
C.
- na, Ho - san - - na,
- na, Ho - san - - na,
T.
- na, Ho - san - - na,
- na, Ho - san - - na,
B.
- na, Ho - san - - na,
- na, Ho - san - - na,

77
S.
- li et ter - ra
full of ech - oes,
glo - - - - -
prais - - - - - -
C.
- li et ter - ra
full of ech - oes,
glo - - - - - -
prais - - - - - -
CHORUS 1
T.
- li et ter - ra
full of ech - oes,
glo - - - - -
prais - - - - -
B.
- li et ter - ra
full of ech - oes,
glo - - - - - -
prais - - - - - -
S.
Ho - san - - na,
Ho - san - - na,
C.
Ho - san - - na,
Ho - san - - na,
CHORUS 2
T.
Ho - san - - na, Ho -
Ho - san - - na, Ho -
B.
Ho - san - - na, Ho - -
Ho - san - - na, Ho - -
77

CHORUS 1
S.
- ri - - a tu - - - - - - a,
- ing Thy glo - - - - - - ry,
C.
- ri - - a tu - - - - - - a,
- ing Thy glo - - - - - - ry,
T.
- ri - - a tu - - - - - - a,
- ing Thy glo - - - - - - ry,
B.
- ri - - a tu - - - - - - a,
- ing Thy glo - - - - - - ry,
CHORUS 2
S.
Ho -
Ho -
C.
T.
- san - - - - - - - - - - - - na,
- san - - - - - - - - - - - - na,
B.
- san - - - - - - - - - - - - na,
- san - - - - - - - - - - - - na,
m.s.
leggiero

S.
T.
B.
CHORUS 2
pp
- san - - na,
- san - - na,
Ho - san - - na,
Ho - san - - na,
Ho - san - -
Ho - san - -
leggiero
78 B
S.
C.
T.
B.
CHORUS 1
ff
Ho - san - na, Ho - san - - na,
Ho - san - na, Ho - san - - na,
Ho - san - - - - - - - na,
Ho - san - - - - - - - na,
Ho - san - na, Ho - san - - na,
Ho - san - na, Ho - san - - na,
Ho - san - - - - - - - na,
Ho - san - - - - - - - na,
CHORUS 2
Ho -
Ho -
- na,
- na,
f
B
78

CHORUS 1
S.
Ho -
Ho -
C.
Ho -
Ho -
T.
Ho -
Ho -
B.
Ho -
Ho -
CHORUS 2
S.
- san - na in ex - cel - - sis,
- san - na in the high - - est,
C.
- san - na in ex - cel - - sis,
- san - na in the high - - est,
T.
- san - na in ex - cel - - sis,
- san - na in the high - - est,
B.
- san - na in ex - cel - - sis,
- san - na in the high - - est,
staccato

CHORUS 1
S.
79
ff
- san - na in ex - cel - - sis, Ho -
- san - na in the high - - est, Ho -
C.
ff
- san - na in ex - cel - - sis, Ho -
- san - na in the high - - est, Ho -
T.
ff
- san - na in ex - cel - - sis, Ho -
- san - na in the high - - est, Ho -
B.
ff
- san - na in ex - cel - - sis, Ho -
- san - na in the high - - est, Ho -
CHORUS 2
S.
ff
Ho -
Ho -
C.
ff
Ho -
Ho -
T.
ff
Ho -
Ho -
B.
ff
Ho -
Ho -
79
ff

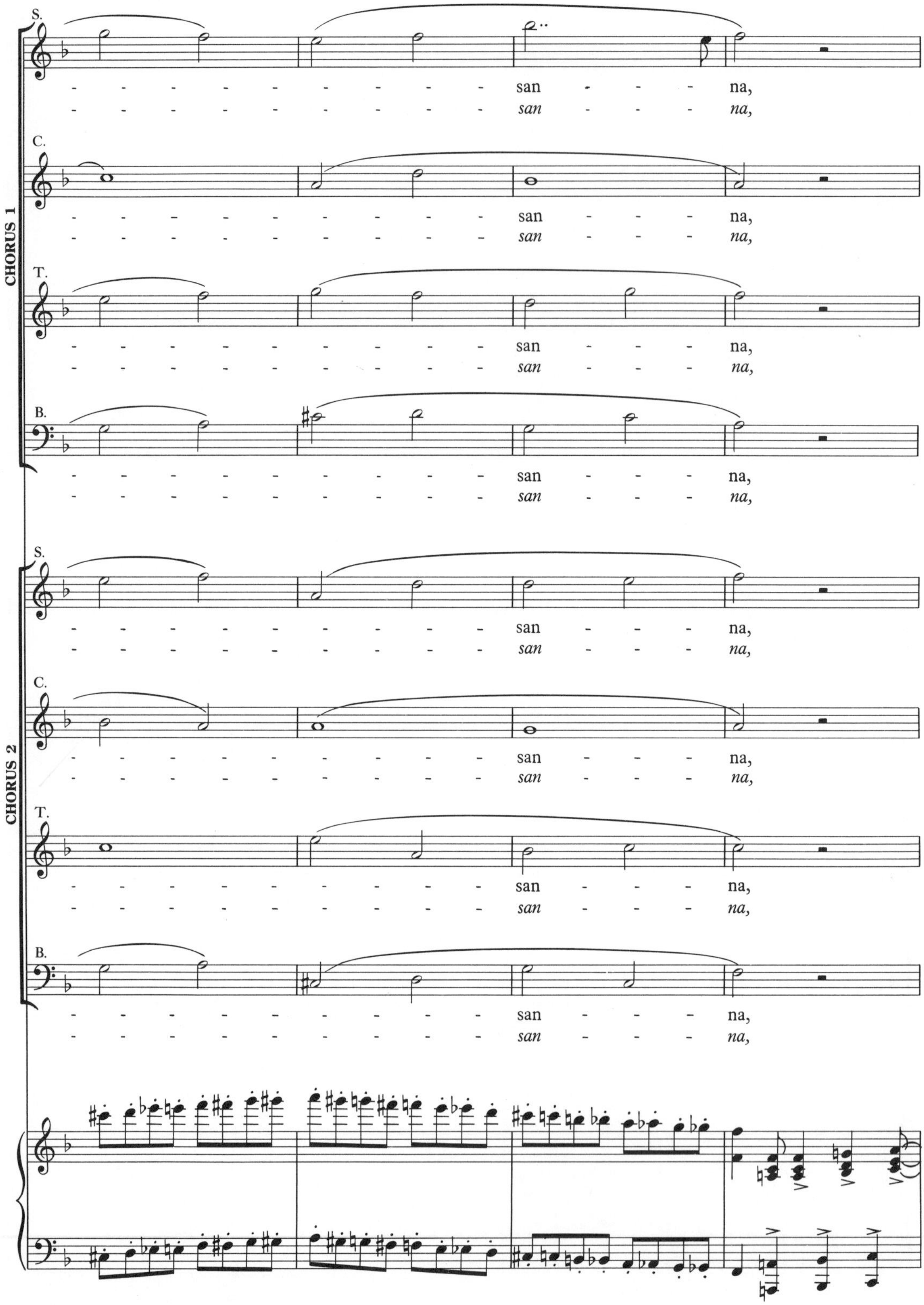
CHORUS 1
S.
san - - - - na,
san - - - - na,
C.
san - - - - na,
san - - - - na,
T.
san - - - - na,
san - - - - na,
B.
san - - - - na,
san - - - - na,
CHORUS 2
S.
san - - - - na,
san - - - - na,
C.
san - - - - na,
san - - - - na,
T.
san - - - - na,
san - - - - na,
B.
san - - - - na,
san - - - - na,

CHORUS 1
S.
Ho-san - na in ex - cel - - sis.
Ho-san - na in the high - - est.
C.
Ho-san - na in ex - cel - - sis.
Ho-san - na in the high - - est.
T.
Ho-san - na in ex - cel - - sis.
Ho-san - na in the high - - est.
B.
Ho-san - na in ex - cel - - sis.
Ho-san - na in the high - - est.
CHORUS 2
S.
Ho-san - na in ex - cel - - sis.
Ho-san - na in the high - - est.
C.
Ho-san - na in ex - cel - - sis.
Ho-san - na in the high - - est.
T.
Ho-san - na in ex - cel - - sis.
Ho-san - na in the high - - est.
B.
Ho-san - na in ex - cel - - sis.
Ho-san - na in the high - - est.

No. 5. AGNUS DEI

(Lamb of God)

Soprano, Mezzo-Soprano and Chorus

80
S.
C.
T.
B.
CHORUS
pp
ppp
A - gnus De - i, A - gnus De - i, qui
Lamb of God, Lamb of God, Thou that
tol - lis pec-ca - ta mun - di, do - na, do - na
bear - est the world's wrong - do - ing, Grant them, grant, Thy

S.
pp
e - is, do - - - na e - - is re - qui-em.
ser - vants, grant them rest for - ev - er - more.
C.
e - is, do - - - na e - - is re - qui-em.
ser - vants, grant them rest for - ev - er - more.
CHORUS
T.
e - is, do - - - na e - - is re - qui-em.
ser - vants, grant them rest for - ev - er - more.
B.
e - is, do - - - na e - - is re - qui-em.
ser - vants, grant them rest for - ev - er - more.
SOP. 81
A - gnus De - i, A - gnus De - i,
Lamb of God, Lamb of God,
MEZZO-SOP.
A - gnus De - i, A - gnus De - i,
Lamb of God, Lamb of God,
81

SOP.
qui tol - lis pec - ca - ta mun - - - - di,
Thou that bear - est the world's wrong - do - - - - ing,
MEZZO-SOP.
qui tol - lis pec - ca - ta mun - - - - di,
Thou that bear - est the world's wrong - do - - - - ing,
SOP.
do - - - - - - na, do - - - - na
grant them, grant, Thy
MEZZO-SOP.
do - - - - - - na, do - - - - na
grant them, grant, Thy
SOP.
pp
e - is, do - - - - na e - - - is re - qui - em;
ser - vants, grant them rest for ev - er - more.
MEZZO-SOP.
pp
e - is, do - - - - na e - - - is re - qui - em;
ser - vants, grant them rest for ev - er - more.

over

S.
pp
do - - - na, do - - - na
Grant them, grant, Thy
C.
pp
do - - - na, do - - - na
Grant them, grant, Thy
CHORUS
T.
pp
do - - - - - - na, do - - - na
Grant them, grant Thy
B.
pp
do -
Grant
pp
pp
S.
pp
e - is, do - - - - - - na e - - - is re - qui - em.
ser - vants, grant them rest for ev - er - more.
C.
pp
e - is, do - - - - - - na e - - - is re - qui - em.
ser vants, grant them rest for ev - er - more.
CHORUS
T.
pp
e - - is re - qui - em, do - na.
ser - - vants rest and peace, grant them.
B.
pp
- na e - is re qui - em, do - na.
them, grant them rest and peace, grant them.
pp

A
82
SOP.
A - gnus De - i, A - gnus De - i, qui
Lamb of God, Lamb of God, Thou that
MEZZO-SOP.
A - gnus De - i, A - gnus De - i, qui
Lamb of God, Lamb of God, Thou that
p dolcissimo
SOP.
tol - lis pec - ca - ta mun - di, do - - - na,
bear - est the world's wrong - do - ing, Help them,
MEZZO-SOP.
tol - lis pec - ca - ta mun - di, do - - - na,
bear - est the world's wrong - do - ing, Help them,
SOP.
pp
do - na e - is, do - na re - qui - em sem - pi - ter - nam;
help Thy ser - vants, grant that they may find rest for ev - er;
M-SOP.
pp
do - na e - is, do - na re - qui - em sem - pi - ter - nam;
help Thy ser - vants, grant that they may find rest for ev - er;

Over

83
S.
p
do - - - - - - na, do - - na
C. Help them, help Thy
do - - - - - - na, do - - na
T. Help them, help Thy
do - - - - - - na, do - na
Help them, help Thy
B.
do - - - - - - na, do - na
Help them, help Thy
CHORUS
83
8
pp
SOP.
do - - na re-qui-em sem-pi-ter - nam,
MEZZO-SOP.
Grant that they may find rest for ev - er,
pp
do - - na re-qui-em sem-pi-ter - nam,
Grant that they may find rest for ev - er,
S.
e - is, do - - na re-qui-em sem-pi-ter - nam,
C. ser - vants, grant that they may find rest for ev - er,
e - is, do - - na re-qui-em sem-pi-ter - nam,
T. ser - vants, grant that they may find rest for ev - er,
e - - is, re - qui - em, do - na, do-
ser - - vants, grant them rest, Oh grant, Oh
B.
e - - is, re - qui - em, do - na,
ser - - vants, grant them rest, grant them,
CHORUS
8
3
pp
p

SOP.
do - na, do - na e - is, re - qui -
and peace never - end - ing, rest and
MEZZO-SOP.
do - na, do - na e - is, re - qui -
and peace never - end - ing, rest and
T.
- na e - is,
grant them rest,
CHORUS
B.
do - na e - is,
Oh grant them rest,
pp
p
SOP.
- em sem - pi - ter - nam.
peace never - end - ing.
M-SOP.
- em sem - pi - ter - nam.
peace never - end - ing.
S.
C.
T.
B.
pp
do - na.
end - ing.
CHORUS
CHORUS SITS

No. 6. LUX AETERNA

(Light forever)

Mezzo-Soprano, Tenor and Bass

MEZZO-SOP.
84
pp
es.
good.
Re - qui -
Rest and
TEN.
Re - qui -
Rest and
BASS
Re - qui-em æ - ter - nam do - na e - - - - is,
Rest and peace for ev - er, Grant them peace, Lord.
84
pp
MEZZO-SOP.
p
- em æ - - ter - nam
peace ev - er - more,
TEN.
- em æ - - ter - nam
peace ev - er - more,
BASS
Re - qui-em æ - ter - nam do - na
Rest and peace for ev - er, Grant Thy
ppp

MEZZO-SOP.
Poco più animato
mf p f
do - na e - is, Do - mi - ne: et lux per -
Grant Thy ser - vants, Lord Our God: and light that
TEN.
mf p f
do - na e - is, Do - mi - ne: et
Grant Thy ser - vants, Lord Our God: and
BASS
f
e - is, Do - mi - ne: et lux per -
ser - vants, Lord Our God: and light that
Poco più animato
pp
f
MEZZO-SOP.
pp
- pe - tu - a, et lux per - pe - tu - a lu - ce - at e - is,
nev - er fades and light that nev - er fades shine down up - on them;
TEN.
pp
lux per - pe - tu - a lu - ce - at
light that nev - er fades shine down up -
BASS
pp
- pe - tu - a, et lux per - pe - tu - a lu - ce - at e - is,
nev - er fades and light that nev - er fades shine down up - on them;
pp

MEZZO-SOP.
dim.
pp
lu - ce - at e - is, Cum Sanc - tis tu - is in æ -
shine down up - on them, with all Thy bless - ed saints for
TEN.
pp
e - - is Cum San - ctis, Cum Sanc - tis tu - is in æ -
- on them, with all Thy saints, all Thy bless - ed saints for
BASS
pp
lu - ce - at e - is, Cum Sanc - tis tu - is in æ -
shine down up - on them, with all Thy bless - ed saints for
dim.
pp
MEZZO-SOP.
dim.
- ter - num, qui - a pi - us es, pi - us es.
ev - er, since that Thou art just, Thou art just.
TEN.
- ter - num, qui - a, qui - a pi - us es.
ev - er, since Thou, since that Thou art just.
BASS
- ter - num, qui - a pi - us es, pi - us es.
ev - er, since that Thou art just, Thou art just.
dim.

A
85
MEZZO-SOP.
a tempo
ppp
dolce
Re - qui - em, Re - qui -
Rest and peace, Rest and
TEN.
ppp
pp
Re - qui - em, Re - qui-
Rest and peace, Rest and
BASS
pp
Re - qui-em æ - ter - nam do - na, do - na e - is,
Rest and peace for - ev - er, grant them rest for ev - er,
A
85
a tempo
pp
MEZZO-SOP.
mf
- em, Re-qui-em æ - ter - nam do - na
peace, Rest and peace for ev - er, Rest for
TEN.
- em, Re-qui-em æ - ter - nam
peace, Rest and peace for ev - er,
BASS
f
Re - qui-em æ - ter - nam, do - na e - is, Do - mi - ne, do -
Rest and peace for ev - er, Rest for ev - er grant them, Lord, rest
mf

B
86
MEZZO-SOP.
dolciss.
e - is, Do - mi - ne. et
ev - er grant them, Lord, and
TEN.
f
do - na e - is.
Rest for ev - er.
BASS
- - na e - is, Do - mi - ne,
for ev - er grant them, Lord.
B
86
pp
p
MEZZO-SOP.
lux per - - pe - - tu - a
light that nev - - er fades
MEZZO-SOP.
lu - - - - - - - ce - - - at
shine down up - - -
p

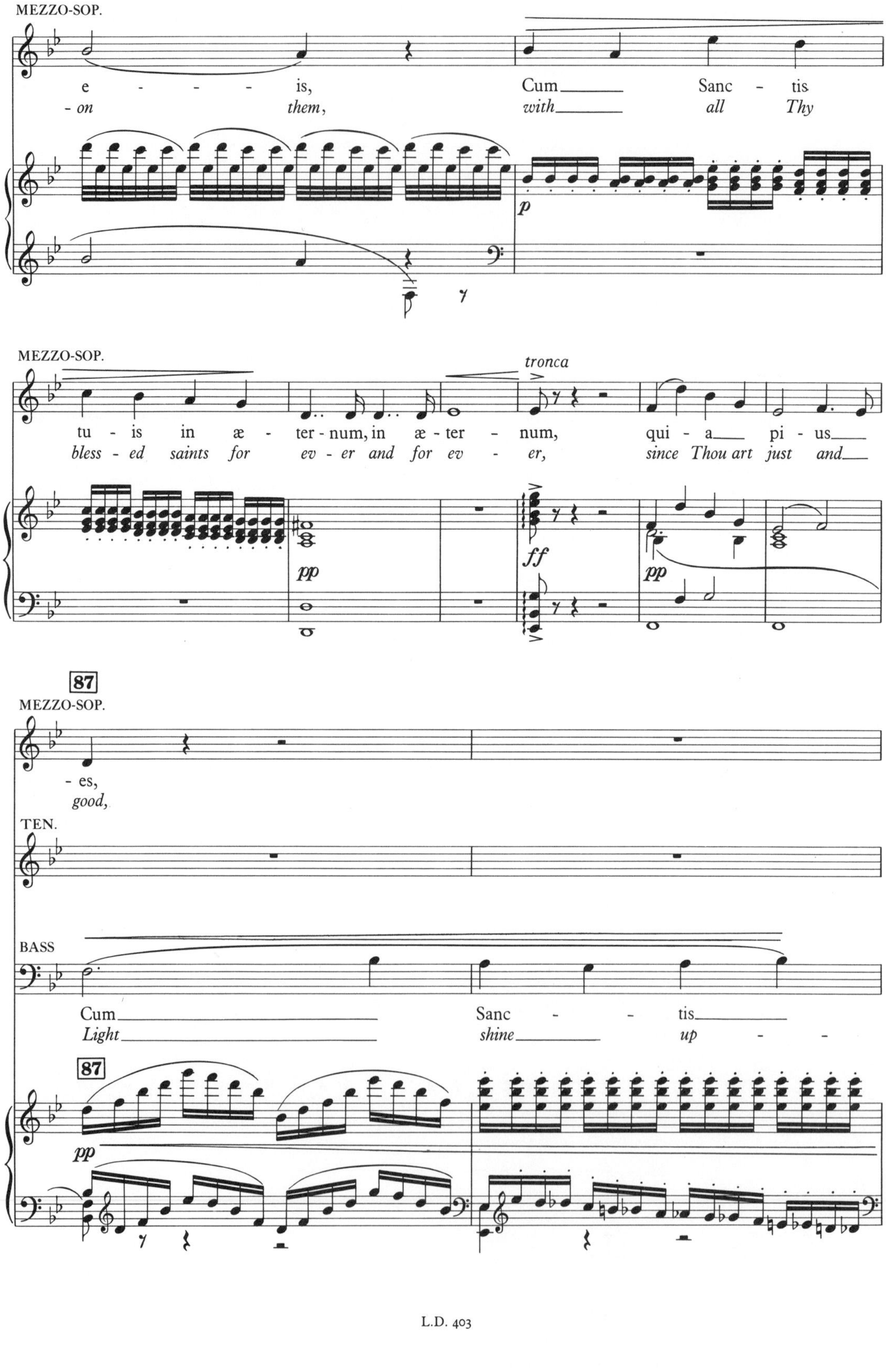
MEZZO-SOP.
e - - - - is, Cum Sanc - tis
- on them, with all Thy
p
MEZZO-SOP.
tronca
tu - is in æ - ter - num, in æ - ter - num, qui - a pi - us
bless - ed saints for ev - er and for ev - er, since Thou art just and
pp
ff
pp
87
MEZZO-SOP.
- es,
good,
TEN.
BASS
Cum Sanc - - tis
Light shine up - -
87
pp

MEZZO-SOP.
in æ-ter - - num,
nev - er fa - - ding
TEN.
Cum Sanc-tis tu - is
Light shine up - on them
BASS
tu - - is in æ -
on them with Thy
MEZZO-SOP.
in æ-ter - -
and for ev - -
TEN.
in æ -
and for
BASS
-ter - num, in æ - ter - - num,
bless - ed saints for ev - - er,

MEZZO-SOP.
- num, Cum Sanc - tis tu - is in æ - ter - -
- er, with all Thy bless - ed saints for ev - -
TEN.
- ter - num, in æ - ter - num,
ev - er, and for ev - er,
BASS
Cum Sanc - tis tu - is in æ - ter - num,
with all Thy bless - ed saints for ev - er,
p
staccato
MEZZO-SOP.
- num, in æ - ter - - - - - - -
- er, and for ev - - - - - - -
TEN.
in æ - ter - - - - - - -
and for ev - - - - - - -
BASS
in æ - ter - - - - - - -
and for ev - - - - - - -

MEZZO-SOP.
pp
-num, qui - a pi - us es, pi - us es, qui - a pi - us
-er, since that Thou art just, Thou art just, since that Thou art
TEN.
pp
-num, qui - a pi - us es, qui - a pi - us
-er, since that Thou art just, since that Thou art
BASS
pp
-num, qui - a pi - us, pi - us
-er, for that Thou art, Thou art
pp
p
C
88
MEZZO-SOP.
p
-es, Cum Sanc - tis tu - is in
just, with all Thy bless - ed Saints ev
TEN.
p
-es, Cum San - ctis
just, with all Thy
BASS
p
es, Cum Sanc - tis tu - is in æ - ter -
just, with all Thy bless - ed saints for ev - er -
C
88
p

MEZZO-SOP.
dim. sempre morendo
æ - ter - num, qui - a pi - us
- - - - er, ev - er, since that Thou art
TEN.
dim. sempre morendo
tu - is in æ - ter - num, qui - - a pi - us
bless - ed saints for ev - er, since that Thou art
BASS
dim. sempre morendo
- num, qui - a pi - us es, qui - - - - a pi - us
- more, since that Thou art just, since that Thou art
p
dim.
sempre morendo
MEZZO-SOP.
mezza voce
89
- es. Lux per - pe - tu - a lu - ce - at e - is,
just. Light for ev - er - more shine down up - on them,
TEN.
pp
- es. Re - qui-em, Re - qui-em
just. Rest and peace, Rest and peace
BASS
pp
- es. Re - qui-em, Re - qui-em
just. Rest and peace, Rest and peace
89
pp

MEZZO-SOP.
lu - ce at e - is, Do - - - mi - ne.
shine down up-on them, Christ the Lord.
TEN.
æ - ter - - - nam.
for ev - - - er.
BASS
æ - ter - - - nam.
for ev - - - er.
dolcissimo con calma senza affrettare
MEZZO-SOP.
TEN.
STAND
BASS
CHORUS RISES
p

No. 7. LIBERA ME

(Lord, deliver me)

Solo for Soprano, Chorus, and final Fugue

S.
pp senza misura
Li - be-ra me, Do - mi - ne, de mor - te æ - ter - na, in di - e il - la tre -
Lord, de - li - ver me out of ev - er - last - ing death, Oh Lord, up - on that day of
C.
pp
Li - be-ra me, Do - mi - ne, de mor - te æ - ter - na, in di - e il - la tre -
Lord de - li - ver me out of ev - er - last - ing death, Oh Lord, up - on that day of
CHORUS
T.
pp
Li - be-ra me, Do - mi - ne, de mor - te æ - ter - na, in di - e il - la tre -
Lord de - li - ver me out of ev - er - last - ing death, Oh Lord, up - on that day of
B.
pp
Li - be-ra me, Do - mi - ne, de mor - te æ - ter - na, in di - e il - la tre -
Lord de - li - ver me out of ev - er - last - ing death, Oh Lord, up - on that day of
senza misura
S.
a tempo
ancora più p
senza misura
a tempo
- men - da; quan - do cœ - li mo - ven - di sunt et ter - ra.
ter - ror, when the earth and the hea - vens shall be sha - ken.
C.
- men - da; quan - do cœ - li mo - ven - di sunt et ter - ra.
ter - ror, when the earth and the hea - vens shall be sha - ken.
CHORUS
T.
- men - da; quan - do cœ - li mo - ven - di sunt et ter - ra.
ter - ror, when the earth and the hea - vens shall be sha - ken.
B.
- men - da; quan - do cœ - li mo - ven - di sunt et ter - ra.
ter - ror, when the earth and the hea - vens shall be sha - ken.
a tempo
senza misura
a tempo

SOP.
Dum ve - ne - ris ju - di -
When Thou shalt come and the
p
SOP.
- ca - re sæ - cu - lum per i - - - - - gnem.
whole world know the fire of judg - - - - - ment.
f
pp stacc.
p
A
90
SOP.
sotto voce
Tre - mens fac - tus sum
Trem - bling, fright - ened and
ppp
SOP.
dim.
e - go et ti - - - - - - - me - o, dum dis -
full of des - pair am I, till the
dim.

SOP.
-cus - sio ve - ne-rit at - - que ven - tu - ra i - -
tri - al shall be at hand, and the wrath, the wrath to
SOP.
- ra; quan - do cœ - li mo-ven - di
come; when the hea - vens and all the
SOP.
sunt et ter - - ra,
earth are sha - - ken,
SOP.
91 B
pp
Tre - mens fac - tus sum
Trem - bling, fright - ened and
f
p dim.
91 B
pp

SOP.
e - go et ti - - - - - - - - - - - - me -
full of des - pair am
SOP.
- o, Tre - mens fac - tus sum e - go, Tre - mens
I, full of ter - ror and great fear, I am
p
SOP.
voce cupa
ppp
pppp
fa - ctus sum e - go, Tre - mens fac - tus sum e - go et
trem - bling with ter - ror, Trem - bling, trem - bling with ter - ror and
pp
m.s.
ppp
pp morendo
SOP.
allarg. e morendo
lunga pausa
92
Allegro Agitato (𝅗𝅥 = 80)
ti - me - o.
dread - ful fear.
92
pp
lunga pausa
ff

S.
C.
T.
B.
CHORUS
ff
Di - es i - ræ, Di - es i - ræ,
Day of an - ger, Day of an - ger
Di - es i - ræ,
Day of an - ger,
Di - es i - ræ,
Day of an - ger,
8

ff
CHORUS
T.
di - - es il - la, di - es
Day of ter - ror, Day of
B.
di - - es il - la, di - es
Day of ter - ror, Day of
93
S.
ter
il
di - - es il
Day of ter
C.
ter
il
di - - es il
Day of ter
T.
ter
il
il
ter
B.
il
ter

S.
- ror,
- la,
- la,
- ror,
f
Di - es
Day of
C.
- ror,
- la,
- la,
- ror,
f
Di - es
Day of
CHORUS
T.
- ror,
- la,
- la,
- ror,
f
Di - es
Day of
B.
f
- la,
- ror,
Di - - - es
Day of
f
S.
i - ræ, di - es il - - - - - - - la,
an - ger, Day of ter - - - - - - - ror,
C.
i - ræ, di - es il - - - - - - - la,
an - ger, Day of ter - - - - - - - ror,
T.
i - ræ, di - es, di - es il - - - - - - - la,
an - ger, Day of, Day of ter - - - - - - - ror,
B.
i - - ræ, di - es, di - es il - - - - - - - la,
an - - ger, Day of, Day of ter - - - - - - - ror,
CHORUS

S.
C.
T.
B.
CHORUS
Di - es i - ræ, di - es
Day of an - ger, Day of
Di - es i - ræ, Di - es, di - es
Day of an - ger, Day of, Day of
Di - es i - ræ, Di - es
Day of an - ger, Day of
il - la,
ter - ror,
94
ff
ca - la - mi -
Day of dis -
f
ca - la - mi - ta - tis, ca - la - mi -
Day of dis - as - ter, Day of dis -

CHORUS
S.
- ta - tis et mi - se - ri - æ,
- as - ter, and of mi - se - ry,
C.
- ta - tis et mi - se - ri - æ,
- as - ter, and of mi - se - ry,
T.
- ta - tis et mi - se - ri - æ,
- as - ter, and of mi - se - ry,
B.
- ta - tis et mi - se - ri - æ,
- as - ter, and of mi - se - ry,
95
CHORUS
S.
di - es ma - gna et a - -
Day most fear - ful, hope - less
C.
di - es ma - gna et a - -
Day most fear - ful, hope - less
T.
di - es ma - gna et a - -
Day most fear - ful, hope - less
B.
di - es ma - gna et a - -
Day most fear - ful, hope - less
95

S.
- ma - ra val - de. Di - es, di - es i - ræ.
and most bit - ter, Day of, Day of an - ger.
C.
- ma - ra val - de. Di - es, di - es i - ræ.
and most bit - ter, Day of, Day of an - ger.
CHORUS
T.
ma - ra val - de. Di - es, di - es i - ræ,
and most bit - ter, Day of, Day of an - ger.
B.
- ma - ra val - de. Di - es i - ræ, di - es il - la, ca - la - mi - ta - tis et mi -
and most bit - ter, Day of an - ger, day of ter - ror, day of dis - as - ter and of
pesante
S.
a tempo
T.
CHORUS
C.
B.
stent. un poco
a tempo
- se - ri - æ, di - es ma - gna et a ma - ra val - de.
mi - se - ry, day most fear - ful and ex - ceed - ing bit - ter.
f a tempo
stent. un poco

96
C
S.
C.
T.
B.
CHORUS
ff
Di - es i - ræ, di - es il - la,
Day of an - ger, Day of ter - ror,
ca - la - mi - ta - tis et mi - se - ri - æ,
Day of dis - as - ter, and of mi - se - ry,

S.
C.
T.
B.
CHORUS
p dim.
Di - es i - ræ, di - es
Day of an - ger, Day of
di es ma - gna, di - es ma - gna
Day most fear - ful, Day most fear - ful
di - es ma - gna, di - es ma - gna
Day most fear - ful, Day most fear - ful
di - es ma - gna, di - es ma - gna
Day most fear - ful, Day most fear - ful
p
dim.

S.
C.
T.
B.
CHORUS
p
pp
il - la, Di - es i - ræ, Di - es
ter - ror, Day of an - ger, Day of
et a - ma - ra, a - ma - ra val - de.
and most bit - ter, fear - ful and bit - ter.
et a - ma - ra, a - ma - ra val - de.
and most bit - ter, fear - ful and bit - ter.
et a - ma - ra, a - ma - ra val - de.
and most bit - ter, fear - ful and bit - ter.
ancora più piano
ancora dim.
m.s.

SOP.
ancora dim.
97
Dum ve - ne-ris ju - di - ca - re
When Thou shalt come and the whole world
S.
i - ræ, Di - es i - ræ, Di - es
an - ger, Day of an - ger, Day of
C.
T.
Di - es i - ræ, Di - es
Day of an - ger, Day of
B.
CHORUS
se - cu lum per i - - - - gnem.
know the fire of judg - - - - ment.
i - ræ, Di - es i - ræ,
an - ger, Day of an - ger,
Di - es i - ræ,
Day of an - ger,
i - ræ, Di - es i - ræ,
an - ger, Day of an - ger,
Di es i - ræ, Di - es i - -
Day of an - ger, Day of an - -
f
pp

S.
C.
T.
B.
CHORUS
Di - es i - ræ,
Day of an - ger,
- ræ, Di - es i -
- ger, Day of an -
ancora più piano
più piano
Di - es i - ræ.
Day of an - ger.
m.d.
morendo
go to page 193

SOP. 98 Andante (♩ = 80)
ppp
espress.
Re - qui - em æ - - - - ter - nam do - na
Rest and peace for - - - - ev - er, Grant, Al -
S.
Re - qui - em, Re - qui-em æ - ter - nam do - na,
Rest and peace, rest and peace e - ter - nal, grant them,
C.
Re - qui - em, Re - qui em æ - ter - nam do - na,
Rest and peace, rest and peace e - ter - nal, Oh grant
T.
Re - qui - em, Re - qui-em æ - ter - nam do - na,
Rest and peace, rest and peace e - ter - nal, Oh grant
B.
Re - qui - em, Re - qui em æ - ter - nam do - na,
Rest and peace, rest and peace e - ter - nal, Oh grant
CHORUS
98 Andante (♩ = 80)
ppp
SOP.
e - is, do - na e - is, e - is, Do - mi - ne, do - -
migh - ty, peace e - ter - nal to their souls, Oh Lord, grant
S.
do - na, do - na, do - na e - is,
grant them, grant them peace e - ter - nal,
C.
do - na, do - na, do - na e - is,
them rest and peace, peace e - ter - nal,
T.
do - na, do - na, do - na e - is,
them rest and peace, peace e - ter - nal,
B.
do - na, do - na, do - na e - is,
them rest and peace, peace e - ter - nal,
CHORUS
ppp

SOP.
cresc.
na, do - na e - is, Do - mi - ne,
them peace e - ter - nal, Lord Our God,
S.
do - na e - is, do - na e - is, Do - mi - ne,
peace e - ter - nal, peace e - ter - nal, Lord Our God,
C.
do - na e - is, do - na e - is, Do - mi - ne,
peace e - ter - nal, peace e - ter - nal, Lord Our God,
T.
do - na e - is, do - na e - is, Do - mi - ne,
peace e - ter - nal, peace e - ter - nal, Lord Our God,
B.
do - na e - is, do - na e - is, Do - mi - ne,
peace e - ter - nal, peace e - ter - nal, Lord Our God,
CHORUS
cresc.
SOP.
ppp dolciss.
portate
et lux per - pe - tu - a lu - ce - at e - is, lu - ce - at
and light for ev - er - more shine down up - on them, shine down up -
S.
ppp
et lux per - pe - tu - a lu - ce - at
and light, light er - ev - more shine down up -
C.
ppp
et lux per - pe - tu - a lu - ce - at
and light, light ev - er - more shine down up -
T.
ppp
et lux per - pe - tu - a lu - ce - at
and light, light ev - er more shine down up -
B.
ppp
et lux per - pe - tu - a lu - ce - at
and light, light ev - er - more shine down up -
CHORUS
ppp

SOP.
S.
C.
T.
B.
CHORUS
e - is, lu - ce - at e - is.
- on them, shine down up - on them.
e - is, et lux per - pe - tu - a lu - ce - at e - is.
- on them, and light for ev - er - more shine down up - on them.
f
dim.
pp
ppp
ancora più p
Re - qui - em æ - ter - nam do - na e - is, Do - mi - ne,
Rest and peace e - ter - nal grant to them, Oh Lord Our God,
Re - qui - em do - na,
Rest and peace, and peace,

SOP.
p e cresc. a poco a poco
et lux per - pe - tu - a lu - ce - at
and light, for ev - er - more shine down up -
S.
et lux, et lux per - pe - tu - a lu - ce - at
and light, and light for ev - er - more shine down up -
C.
et lux, et lux per - pe - tu - a lu - ce - at
and light, and light for ev - er - more shine down up -
T.
et lux, et lux per - pe - tu - a lu - ce - at
and light, and light for ev - er - more shine down up -
B.
et lux, et lux per - pe - tu - a lu - ce - at
and light, and light for ev - er - more shine down up -
CHORUS
p e cresc. a poco a poco
SOP.
morendo
pp
pppp
e - is. Re - qui - em, Re - qui - em.
- on them. Peace and rest, peace and rest.
S.
C.
T.
B.
morendo

99 D
SOP. lunga pausa
senza misura
Li - be-ra me, Do-mi-ne, de mor-te æ - ter - na, in di-e il-la tre-
Lord, de-li-ver me out of ev-er-last-ing death, Oh Lord, up-on that day of
f
senza misura
SOP. Moderato (♩ = 100)
a tempo
ff
-men - da; quan - do cœ - li mo-ven-di sunt et
ter - ror, when the earth and the hea-vens. shall be
a tempo
ff
E
100
Allegro risoluto (𝅗𝅥 = 116)
f
ter - ra.
sha - ken.
C.
CHORUS
Li - be-ra me, Do-mi-ne, de
Lord, do Thou de - li-ver me from
mor - te æ - ter - na, in di-e il - la tre-men -
death ev - er-last - ing up-on that day of dis-as -
ff

S.
CHORUS
Li - be - ra me, Do - mi - ne, de mor - te æ - ter - na,
Lord, do Thou de - li - ver me from death ev - er - last - ing
C.
- da; quan - do, quan - do cœ - - - - - li mo -
- ster, that day when the hea - - - - - vens and
S.
in di - e il - la tre - men - - - - da, quan - do, quan - do
up - on that day of dis - as - - - - ter, that day when the
F
101
C.
- ven - di sunt et ter - - - - - - - ra, Dum ve - ne - ris
all the earth are sha - - - - - - ken, when Thou shalt come
T.
B.
Li - be - ra me, Do - mi - ne, de
Lord, do Thou de - li - ver me from

S.
C.
T.
B.
CHORUS
cœ - - - li mo - ven - di sunt et ter - -
hea - - - vens and all the earth are sha - -
ju - di - ca - - - - - - - - re sæ - cu - lum per i - -
for the tri - - - - - - - - al by the fires of judg - -
mor - te æ - ter - na, in di - e il - la tre - men - -
death ev - er - last - ing up - on that day of dis - as - -
ff
- - - - - ra, Dum ve - ne - ris ju - di - ca - - - - -
- - - - - ken, when Thou shalt come for the tri - - - - -
- gnem, Dum ve - ne - ris ju - di -
- ment, When Thou shalt come for the
f
Li - be - ra me, Do - mi - ne, de mor - te æ - ter - na,
Lord, do Thou de - li - ver me from death ev - er - last - ing
- da; quan - do, quan - do cœ - - - - li mo - -
- ter, that day when the hea - - - - vens and

S.
re sæ - cu - lum per i - gnem.
al by the fires of judg - ment.
C.
ca - re sæ - cu - lum per i - gnem. Li -
tri - al by the fires of judg - ment. Lord,
T.
in di - e il - la tre - men - da;
up - on that day of dis - as - ter.
B.
ven - di sunt et ter - ra. Li - be - ra me,
all the earth are sha - ken. Lord, do Thou de -
CHORUS
f
102
S.
Li - be - ra me, Do - mi -
Lord, do Thou de - li - ver
C.
be - ra me, Do - mi - ne,
de - li - ver me, Lord, save me,
T.
Li - be - ra, li - be - ra me, de mor - te æ -
Do Thou de - li - ver me from death ev - er -
B.
Do - mi - ne, de mor - te, de mor - te æ - ter -
li - ver me from death, out of death ev - er - last -
CHORUS
102

S.
C.
T.
B.
CHORUS
f
ff
p
-ne, Do - - - mi - ne, Do - -
me, Save me, Lord, Save
Li - be - ra me, Li - be - ra me,
De - li - ver me, De - li - ver me,
-ter - na in di - e il - la tre -
-last - ing, from death in that day of
-na in di - - - e, in di - - - -
-ing in that day, in that
- - mi - ne, Li - be - ra me, Do - mi - ne, de
me, Lord. Lord, do Thou de - li - ver me from
de mor - te æ - ter - na,
from ev - er - last - ing death,
-men - - - - - - da, Li - - -
ter - - - - - - ror. Save
-e tre - men - - - da,
day of ter - - - ror,

S.
C.
T.
B.
CHORUS
mor - te æ - ter -
death__ ev - er - last -
Li - be - ra me, Do - mi - ne, de mor - te æ -
Lord, do Thou de - li - ver me from death__ ev - er -
- be - ra me,
me, Oh Lord.
p
in di - e__ il - la tre - men - da;
in that day,__ that day of ter - ror;
103
- na, in di - e il - la,__ il - la tre -
- ing, up - on that day of fear,__ that day of
- ter - - - - - na, in di - e__ il - la tre -
- last - - - - - ing, in that day,__ that day of
Li - be - ra me, Do - mi - ne, de mor - te æ - ter - na;
Lord, do Thou de - li - ver me from death ev - er - last - ing;
quan - do cœ - li mo - ven - di
when the whole__ earth and heav'n shall
103

S.
C.
T.
B.
CHORUS
(poco a poco molto cresc.)
- men - da;
ter - ror,
- men - da; quan - do cœ - li mo - ven - di
ter - ror, when the whole earth and heav'n shall
(più f)
quan - do cœ - - - li mo - ven - - - - di sunt et
when the hea - - - vens and all the earth are
(f)
sunt, quan - do cœ - li mo - ven - di
quake, when the whole earth and heav'n shall
(poco a poco molto cresc.)
ff
Li - be - ra me, Li - be - ra me,
Lord, de - li - ver me, Lord, de - li - ver me,
sunt, quan - do cœ - li, quan - do
quake, when the whole earth, when the
ter - ra, quan - do cœ - li, quan - do
sha - ken, when the whole earth, when the
sunt, quan - do cœ - li, quan - do
quake, when the whole earth, when the

104
S.
Li - be - ra me, Li - be - ra me, Do - mi - ne, de
Lord, de - li - ver me, Lord, do Thou de - li - ver me from
C.
cœ - li mo - ven - di sunt,
whole earth and heav'n shall quake,
T.
cœ - li mo - ven - di sunt,
whole earth and heav'n shall quake,
B.
f
cœ li mo - ven - di sunt, quan - do
whole earth and heav'n shall quake, when the
CHORUS
104
f

S.
mor - te æ - ter - na in di - e il - la tre -
death ev - er - last - ing upon that day of dis -
C.
quan - do cœ - li mo - ven - di sunt et
when the hea - vens and all the earth are
T.
mo - ven - di sunt, mo - ven - di sunt et
when the hea - vens and all the earth are
B.
cœ - li mo - ven - di sunt et
hea - vens and all the earth are
CHORUS

G
105
S.
C.
T.
B.
CHORUS
- men - - - da;
- as - - - ter;
ter - - - ra;
sha - - - ken;
ju - di - ca - re
Thou shalt come and
ter - - - ra;
sha - - - ken;
Dum ve -
When Thou
ter - - - ra; Dum ve - ne - ris ju - di - ca - re
sha - - - ken; When Thou shalt come and the whole world
ju - di - ca - re sæ - cu - lum per i - gnem,
All the world shall know the fire of judg - ment,
ju - di - ca - re sæ - cu - lum per i - - - gnem, per
all the world shall know the fire of judg - - ment, of
- ne - ris ju - di - ca - re sæ - cu -
shalt come and the world shall know the
sæ - cu - lum per i - gnem, ju - di - ca - re sæ - cu - lum per
know the fire of judg - ment, all the world shall know the fire of

S.
C.
T.
B.
CHORUS
(mp) (poco a poco dim.)
ju - di - ca - re sæ - cu - lum per
All the world shall know the fire of
(mp)
i - gnem, ju - di - ca - re sæ - cu - lum per i - - -
judg - ment; all the world shall know the fire of judg - - -
(mp)
- lum per i - gnem, ju - di - ca - re
fire of judg - ment, all the world shall
i - - gnem,
judg - - ment.
m.s.
(poco a poco dim.)
i - gnem, Do - mi - ne, Do - mi - ne,
judg - ment. De - li - ver me, Oh Lord,
- gnem. Li - be - ra me, Li - be - ra,
- ment. Lord, de - li - ver me, Lord, de - li - ver
sæ - cu - lum per i - - gnem. Do - mi - ne, Do - - -
know the fire of judg - - ment. De - li - ver me,
mp
ju - di - ca - re sæ - cu - lum per i - - - - - - -
All the world shall know the fire of judg - - - - - - -
p dolce

WATCH FOR SOLO SPEED.

SOP.
- ne de mor - - te, de mor - - te æ - ter - -
S. Lord, Oh save me from ev - - er - last - ing -
Li - be - ra me
C. Lord, de - li - ver me
te æ - ter - - - - - - - -
T. ev - er - last - - - - - - -
mor - - - - - - - te æ - ter - -
death ev - er - last - -
B.
de mor - - te æ - ter - -
from death for - ev - -
CHORUS
SOP.
- na, Li - be - ra me, Li - be - ra
S. death, De - li - ver me, de - li - ver
in di - e il - - - la, in di - e il - la tre -
C. up - on that dread day, up - on that day of dis -
- na, in di - e il - - la, in di - e il - la tre -
T. - ing up - on that dread day, up - on that day of dis -
- na in di - e il - - la, in di - e il - la tre -
- ing up - on that dread day, up - on that day of dis -
B.
- na, Li - be - ra me, Li - be - ra
- er. De - li - ver me, de - li - ver
CHORUS

SOP.
me, Li - be - ra me,
me, de - li - ver me,
S.
- men - da quan - do cœ - li mo - ven - di sunt et ter -
- as - ter when the whole earth and all the hea - vens shall
C.
- men - da quan - do cœ - li mo - ven - di sunt et ter -
- as - ter when the whole earth and all the hea - vens shall
T.
- men - da quan - do cœ - li mo - ven - di sunt et ter -
- as - ter when the whole earth and all the hea - vens shall
B.
me, Li - be - ra me de mor - te æ - ter -
me. De - li - ver me, Oh Lord from ev - er - last - ing
CHORUS
SOP.
107
Li - be - ra me, Li - be - ra me, Li - be - ra
de - li - ver me, de - li - ver me, de - li - ver
S.
- ra, Li - be - ra me, Li - be - ra me, Li - be - ra
quake, De - li - ver me, de - li - ver me, de - li - ver
C.
- ra, quan - do cœ - li mo -
quake, when all hea - ven and
T.
- ra, Li - be - ra, Li - be - ra me de
quake, Save me, Lord, save me, Lord, from
B.
- na in di - e, in di - e tre -
death in that day, in that day of
CHORUS
107

SOP.
me de mor - te æ - ter -
me from death ev - er - last -
S.
me de mor - te æ - ter -
me from death ev - er - last -
C.
- ven - di sunt, mo - ven - di sunt et
earth shall quake, hea - ven and earth are
CHORUS
T.
mor - te æ - ter - na in di - e il - la tre - men -
e - ter - nal death in that dread day, that day of ter -
B.
- men - da, quan - do cœ - li mo - ven - di sunt,
ter - ror, when the hea - vens and all the earth,
f
SOP.
108
- na, quan - do cœ - li mo - ven - di sunt,
- ing when the hea - vens and all the earth
S.
- na, quan - do cœ - li mo - ven - di sunt,
- ing when the hea - vens and all the earth
C.
ter - ra, mo - ven - di sunt,
sha - ken, and all the earth
CHORUS
T.
- da, quan - do cœ - li mo - ven - di sunt,
- ror, when the hea - vens and all the earth
B.
quan - do cœ - li, quan - do cœ - li, quan - do
when the hea - vens, when the hea - vens, when the
f
108

SOP.
S.
C.
T.
B.
CHORUS
mo - ven - di sunt, mo - ven - di sunt,
when heav'n and earth, when heav'n and earth,
cœ - li mo - ven - di sunt, quan - do
hea - vens and all the earth, when the
quan - do cœ - li mo - ven - di sunt et ter - ra
when the hea - vens and all the earth are sha - ken.
cœ - li mo - ven - di sunt et ter - ra
high heav'n and all the earth are sha - ken.
ppp
ff
TURN PAGE

109
S.
Li - be - ra me,
Lord, do Thou de -
C.
Li - be - ra me, Do - mi - ne, de
Lord, do Thou de - li - ver me from
T.
Li - be - ra me, Do - mi - ne, de mor - te æ -
Lord, do Thou de - li - ver me from death ev - er -
B.
Li - be - ra me, Do - mi - ne, de mor - te æ - ter -
Lord, do Thou de - li - ver me from death, from e - ter - nal
CHORUS
109
Do - mi - ne, de mor - te æ - ter - na in di - e
- li - ver me from death ev - er - last - ing up - on that
mor - te æ - ter - na in di - e il - la tre -
death, from e - ter - nal death in that day, that day of
- ter - na in di - e il - la tre - men - da,
- last - ing up - on that day of dis - as - ter,
- na in di - e il - la tre - men - da,
death in that day, that day of ter - ror,

S.
il - la tre - men - da, Li - be - ra me, Do - mi - ne, de
day of dis - as - ter, Lord, do Thou de - li - ver me from
C.
- men - da,
ter - ror,
Li - be - ra me,
Lord, do Thou de -
CHORUS
T.
Li - be - ra me, Do - mi - ne, de mor - te in di - e
Lord, do Thou de - li - ver me from death, from e - ter - nal
B.
Li - be - ra me, Do - mi - ne, de mor - te æ -
Lord, do Thou de - li - ver me from death ev - er -
S.
110
mor - te æ - ter - na in di - e il - la tre -
death from e - ter - nal death up - on that day of dis -
C.
Do - mi - ne, de mor - te æ - ter - na in di - e tre -
- li - ver me from death ev - er - last - ing in that day of
CHORUS
T.
il - la, il - la tre - men - da,
death in that day of ter - ror,
B.
- ter - na in di - e il - la tre men - - -
- last - ing up - on that day of dis - as - - -
110

★These bars always *sotto voce* and sung only by few voices.
For the Chorus 4 Sopranos, 4 Contraltos, 4 Tenors and 4 Basses will suffice.

SOP.
Do - mi-ne, de mor - te, de mor - te
- li - ver me from death, from death
S.
pp
sunt et ter - ra, Li - be - ra, Li - be -
heav'ns are sha - ken, Save me, Lord, Save me,
C.
Li - be-ra me, Li - be-ra me, Li - be-ra
Lord, de - li - ver me, Lord, de - li - ver me, Lord, de - li - ver
CHORUS
T.
ppppp
Li - be - ra me
Save me from death
B.
ppppp
ter - ra, Li - be - ra me
sha - ken. Save me from death
SOP.
111
æ - ter - na in di - e il - la tre -
ev - er - last - ing up on that dread day of
S.
- ra, Li - be - ra me, Li - be - ra me,
Lord, Save me Oh Lord, Lord, Oh save me,
C.
me, Li - be-ra me Do - mi - ne, de mor - te æ -
me, Lord, de - li - ver me, Oh Lord, from death for
CHORUS
T.
de mor - te in di - e il - la, il - la tre
for ev - er up-on that dread day, that day of
B.
de mor - te in di - e tre -
for ev - er in that day of
111

SOP.
ppp
men - - - da. Do - mi - ne,
ter - - - ror. Lord, Our God,
S.
Do - mi - ne.
Save me, Lord.
C.
ter - - - na.
ev - - - er.
CHORUS
T.
men - - - da.
ter - - - ror.
B.
men - - - da.
ter - - - ror.
pp
Do - mi - ne, Li - be - ra me de
Lord, Our God, Lord, de - li - ver me from
m.d.
mor - te æ - ter - na in di - - e tre -
death, from death for ev - er up - on that day of
m.s.

SOP.
112
- men - da.
ter - ror.
S.
C.
T.
B.
CHORUS
Tutti
sotto voce
pp
Dum
When
cominciando pppp
Dum ve - ne - ris ju - di - ca - re sæ - cu - lum per
When Thou shalt come, then shall man be tried by fires of
cominciando ppp
ve - ne - ris,
Thou shalt come,
i - gnem, Dum ve - ne - ris ju - di - ca - re sæ - cu - lum per
judg - ment, When Thou shalt come, then shall man be tried by fires of
poco cresc.
when

S.
C.
T.
B.
CHORUS
cresc.
ve - ne - ris ju - di - ca - re
Thou shalt come, then shall man - kind
i - gnem, ju - di - ca - re sæ - cu - lum, ju - di - ca - re
judg - ment, Then shall man be tried by fires, Then shall man be
poco cresc.
ancora cresc.
sæ - cu - lum per i - gnem,
know the fires of judg - ment,
sæ - cu - lum per i - gnem, Do - mi - ne,
know the fires of judg - ment, Oh Lord Our
sæ - cu - lum, sæ - cu - lum per i - gnem, Do - mi - ne,
tried by fires, tried by fires of judg - ment, Oh Lord Our

S.
ff tutta forza
113
Do - mi - ne, Do-mi-ne, Do - mi - ne, Li-be-ra, Li - be - ra, Li-be-ra
God, Oh, Lord, de-li-ver me, Oh, Lord, de-li-ver me, Oh, Lord, de-li-ver
C.
T.
B.
ff
CHORUS
ff tutta forza
SOP.
f
Li - be - ra me,
Oh, save me, Lord,
me de mor - te æ - ter - na in
me from death ev - er - last - ing in
me de mor - te æ - ter - na in di -
me from death ev - er - last - ing in that
me, Li - be - ra me de mor - te æ -
me, de - li - ver me from death ev - er -

SOP.
de mor - te æ - ter
from death ev - er last
S.
di - e il - la tre - men
that day, that day of ter
C.
di - e il - la tre - men
that day, that day of ter
T.
- e, di - e il - la tre - men
day, in that dread day of ter
B.
- ter - na, in il - la tre - men
- last - ing in that day of ter
CHORUS
ff
114
- na,
- ing,
Li
Save
- da,
- ror.
espress.
p
pp
BOOKS DOWN
5 bars memory

SOP.
be - ra me,
me, Oh Lord,
S.
ppp
Li - be - ra me,
Save me, Oh Lord,
C.
Li - be - ra me,
Save me, Oh Lord,
T.
Li - be - ra me,
Save me, Oh Lord,
B.
CHORUS
pp
ppp
S.
pppp
Li - be - ra
Save me, Oh
C.
ppp
Li - be - ra
Save me, Oh
T.
ppp
Li - be - ra
Save me, Oh
B.
ppp
Li - be - ra
Save me, Oh
CHORUS
ppp

SOP.
senza misura
Li - be - ra me, Do - mi - ne, de mor - te æ - ter - na, in di - e il - la tre -
Lord, de - li - ver me out of ev - er - last - ing death, Oh Lord, up - on that day of
S.
pppp
me,
Lord.
C.
pppp
me,
Lord.
T.
pppp
me,
Lord.
B.
pppp
me,
Lord.
CHORUS
senza misura
SOP.
a tempo
poco allarg.
pp
morendo
pppp
- men - da,
ter - ror,
Li - be - ra me,
Save me, Oh Lord.
Li - be - ra me.
Save me, Oh Lord.
S.
C.
T.
B.
Li - be - ra me,
Save me, Oh Lord.
Li - be - ra me.
Save me, Oh Lord.
ppp a tempo
col canto
ppp poco allarg.
morendo